FOR YOU, MOM

THANKS are due to the many people who generously shared their steam clock memories, their time, and their expertise. In particular to my buddy Ray Saunders, for patiently answering endless questions and setting me straight time and again on matters historical and horological. To Jon Ellis, for his approachability, candor, and behind-the-scenes revelations, not to mention thinking up the idea of a steam clock in the first place, nurturing the project, and just being the right guy in the right place at the right time. To Mike Spence, talented metal sculptor and generous host, who helped put the clock together and filled in many of the gaps in Ray Saunders's memories and records.

Special thanks to all the visionaries and volunteers, at the start and over the years, without whom there would be no Gastown Steam Clock story to write; and to all visitors and admirers without whom ... well, if no one comes to see the clock, does the whistle make a noise?

Any writer's works attest as much to his choice of family, friends, and collaborators as to his writing talent. So, when I say thanks to my writing group for their advice and encouragement, especially Karalee and Mary Ann for advice above and beyond (women really are better with words); to the Burnaby Writers Society, especially Eileen for her velvet-gloved fist; to Georgiana in California for early encouragement; to my writing buddy Pete, daughter Jenn, and especially dedicated first reader and other daughter JenPow; to my men's team for the push, to Wolf and buddy Bernie for sharing their clock experiences; when I say thanks to these and any I've missed, you should all know those thanks come from a very sincere place— somewhere about dead centre in my heart.

A special thanks to the patient people whose skills and experience turned a draft into a work of art: Joyce Gram, editor+, and Valerie Thai, book and cover designer and graphics artiste, and Jorge Rocha, Friesens' Printing Rep extraordinaire.

Not the least, thanks to my one-person focus group for years of support and patience far beyond the call of duty or marriage vows—and for some great pointers and practical insights without which this book would be boring in many places where it isn't. So, if you too find it interesting, think good thoughts at my sweet Leagh.

Daryl R. Stennett
August 2011

BEHIND THE STEAM

THE INSIDE STORY OF THE GASTOWN STEAM CLOCK

DARYL R. STENNETT

Library and Archives Canada Cataloguing in Publication

Stennett, Daryl R., 1944-
    Behind the Steam : the inside story of the Gastown
steam clock / Daryl R. Stennett.

Issued also in an electronic format.

ISBN 978-0-9868893-0-1

    1. Clocks and watches--British Columbia--Vancouver.
2. Clocks and watches--British Columbia--Vancouver--Design
and construction. 3. Steam-engines--British Columbia--
Vancouver--Design and construction. I. Title.

TS548.S74 2011   681.1'13   C2011-904282-7

pellucid expressions publishing

5217 Chartwell Road
Sechelt, B.C. V0N 3A2
Canada

Cover art and book design by Valerie Thai, www.cabinandcub.com

Edited by Joyce Gram, www.gramediting.com

Drawings and photographs provided by Raymond L. Saunders except where noted
Photo credits listed at the end of the book

Printed and bound in Canada by Friesens Corporation, Altona, Manitoba

Contents

Gastown Steam Clock

Components.

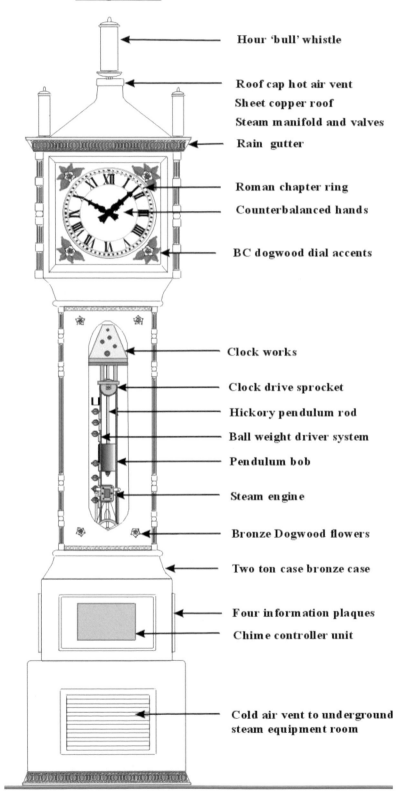

Hour 'bull' whistle

Roof cap hot air vent
Sheet copper roof
Steam manifold and valves
Rain gutter

Roman chapter ring
Counterbalanced hands

BC dogwood dial accents

Clock works

Clock drive sprocket

Hickory pendulum rod

Ball weight driver system

Pendulum bob

Steam engine

Bronze Dogwood flowers

Two ton case bronze case

Four information plaques
Chime controller unit

Cold air vent to underground
steam equipment room

THE WINDS
OF CHANGE

Water Street Improvement Project
A co-operative project of the City of Vancouver
and the merchants of Gastown

Contractor

Imperial Paving Limited
4781 Byrne Road, Burnaby, B.C.

Sub Contractors

Concrete... Castle Concrete Ltd.
Brickwork... Burrard Tile Ltd.
Electrical... Ricketts Sewell Electric Ltd.
Stonework... Mahovlich Stone Masonry Ltd.

Site of the Gastown steam clock

Designed and built by

Ray. Saunders

and

Doug Smith

Completion scheduled for the fall of 1977

WATER STREET AT CAMBIE

The Water Street renovation presented an opportunity to the private utility, Central Heat Distribution Limited.

With the street torn up already, they could expedite a planned expansion of their distribution system at a considerable saving.

THE WINDS OF CHANGE

In the flower-power years of the 1960s and '70s, Vancouver earned its reputation as a forward-thinking, peace-loving city. Vancouverites pioneered in organizing for global peace. They were instrumental in stopping nuclear testing in the Aleutian and Polynesian Islands and at the United Nations. Greenpeace was born here. Vancouver became an official nuclear-free city in 1983.

A lesser-known but far-reaching side effect came in the form of a change in another attitude. In the flower-power years, the mood in British Columbia swung in support of preserving a public heritage, especially buildings with a unique history. The government even revised a little-used provincial law to prevent destruction of Vancouver's older buildings.

In Gastown, the oldest part of Vancouver, long-held plans for demolishing many of the buildings shrivelled and died. Property owners scrambled to find affordable alternatives to their ambitious, now-defunct renewal schemes for the area.

Meanwhile, retail businesses in Gastown struggled; they sought the City of Vancouver's support to attract more customers to their streets. The city see-sawed, pushed in one direction by commercial interests and pulled in another by public sentiment. For several years there was a great deal of uncertainty, no shared vision, and little money to fund any improvements they could agree to.

About the same time, an innovative would-be architect, Jon Ellis, came to Vancouver from Colorado, innocently expecting a plethora of architectural job opportunities. And nearby, a money-losing private utility with a new, community-minded president set out to save a few bucks by adding a manhole and some vent pipes to the middle of a sidewalk. In another part of town, a young newspaper reporter

THE SIXTIES HAPPENING

Love was in the air! Income levels rose and horizons expanded in almost every field. The times, they were a-changin', and nowhere more than in Vancouver, Canada's centre of flower-power and social activism. The transformation in social values generated new political and urban priorities. Governments and public institutions had to adapt or risk a footnote's fate.

Establishments and vested interests were dragged along for the ride. Successful city bureaucrats woke up one morning to find themselves defending waning priorities. City politicians were left groping to retain control of the city's liability risk and expense budgets. In all that confusion, quite a head of steam built up around the Gastown situation.

FLOWER POWER
The Hari Krishna love Gastown.

discovered an entrepreneur to write about—a metal sculptor who combined watch repair skills with a passion for old clocks in his art, producing unusual and eye-catching clock-sculptures.

Few people would discern the makings of an international icon in this array of seemingly unrelated events. Yet an aspiring architect with a stubborn streak and a crazy idea joined an artist with horological tendencies and the two created a unique, working work of art. They were assisted by four innovative property owners,[1] a group of nearly broke business men and women, a long parade of contributors, and many volunteers who liked a foolish idea and wanted to help.

And all to conceal two vent pipes (count them: one, two) rising from a sidewalk in Gastown.

A GASTOWN AND STEAM CLOCK PREHISTORY

VENT OPENING

And rising through the centre of the cement foundation: wiring connections, steam pipes, and anchor bolts also wait for the steam clock.

Vancouver's first building[2] was a saloon. In September 1867, word spread along the south shore of Burrard Inlet that some fellow in a canoe had landed not far to the west of Stamp's lumber mill, and he had a barrel of whiskey. The fellow was Jack Deighton, soon to be known by all as "Gassy Jack" in appreciation of his verbal enthusiasm.

Jack knew how to win friends and motivate volunteer labour. For free drinks, he had himself a saloon and residence built in a single day. It was built by a bunch of men—hard-working, thirsty men—who toiled at the lumber mill. True, it wouldn't come up to modern building codes, but it kept the rain out. And, with the help of his native wife, her mother, aunt, a cousin, and a dog, Jack planted the seeds of a city. Gassy Jack—or his whiskey—was popular, as was attested to by the people's choice of a name for their burgeoning waterhole—Gastown.

Alcohol may not do much for germinating real seeds, but it appears to have had a salutary effect on a budding city, as new arrivals soon started to build around Jack's saloon. Europe's hunger for lumber may have helped, as did British Columbia's own gold rush, and the saloon grew into a prosperous town. Gastown was surveyed and formally named Granville in 1870, but the Gastown sobriquet hung on. No one called it Granville until about 1880, and then only for a few years.

The city's growth to prominence received a boost and a new name when the city was chosen to be the Pacific terminus for the nation-building Canadian Pacific Railway (CPR). An expatriate American like Jon Ellis, William Cornelius Van Horne was hired to eliminate corruption that threatened the railroad and to complete its construction on time and on budget. Van Horne wanted the terminus of the CPR to be called Vancouver, and in 1886, a petition to the government in Victoria was granted and the City of Vancouver came into being. Until, that is, June 13, 1886, when a forest-clearing fire escaped its confines and, encouraged by a stiff breeze, burned the whole place to the last toothpick, along with twenty or so of its unfortunate inhabitants.

Undaunted, those plucky pioneers just built the town again. It boggles the mind how fast the forest was turned into a real city. There are recipes that take longer to prepare. In less than a year, the place was bigger and better than ever.

Arrival of the Canadian Pacific Railway provided the impetus for more and better buildings and created more than one fortune from land speculation. It's true! Modern British Columbia was built on greed. CPR pamphlets promoting Vancouver properties appeared in some unlikely places: Arizona, for example, where the US cavalry apparently turned up a whole bundle of them during a raid on an Apache village![3]

Even Rudyard Kipling got in on the action. He liked the place. By 1907, the world-renowned writer had visited Vancouver three

FIVE WEEKS AFTER THE FIRE

Businesses being rebuilt: Burrard Hotel, Tom Dunn Hardware, Grant & Arkell, Dietz (sp?) Winch, Daily News (on Hastings Street), Sekl's Furniture Store, Dougall House, Tom McDonald (on Pender Street), Mathison the Printer (on Hastings Street), Cosmopolitan Hotel, Mizony's Restaurant, F.W. Hart Furniture, Tilley's (sp?) Book Store and the Telephone Exchange

times and purchased property at the southeast corner of East 11th Avenue and Fraser Street.[4] Indeed, in those days Gastown epitomized the phrase "young and vibrant." Following that energetic start, however, development moved west and south, bypassing Gastown.

Sixty years later, Vancouver was a fast-growing west-coast seaport, the jewel of British Columbia, the city that Canadians from coast to coast thought of as the sparkling centrepiece of Canada's Lotus Land[5] and its gateway to the Pacific.

Brash and bold, Vancouver was beginning to sense greatness in its future. But downtown, the city core had moved farther away from its origins. Left behind was a sadly neglected and still deteriorating commercial area. After more than sixty years of decline, Gastown now cast a dark shadow on the city's rosy public image. It was Vancouver's skid row. The situation cried out for change.

A New Vision

A REPUTATION

Vancouver was considered innovative, off-the-wall original, or whacko, depending on how many provincial borders lay between the city and the person doing the considering.

The rabid revolutionaries of the Community Arts Council took action! The Exposition Gallery had been located by its owner, Henk Vander Horst, in a converted warehouse in the middle of the skid row area. Arch Arts Council pot-stirrer (and civic-minded) Evelyn MacKechnie took advantage of that fact and organized a Gastown Walking Tour. In September 1968, the Arts Council invited hundreds of people to a party at an art gallery. The catch, of course, was that the wine and hors d'oeuvres came packaged with the eye-opening trek—through the slum—that revealed Vancouver's living history.

Some two hundred people were toured by shank's mare to all of the historic sites the Arts Council could think to show them, before hiking back to the art gallery for a sip and a nosh. Slipped into the schmoozing was "Would you mind helping us with this little idea we have to make this historic slum into a vibrant work of art?"

Probably out of fear of losing the next election—though they deserve credit for some smart thinking and wise decision-making—city council agreed to forgo freeways and pursue a more neighbourhood-friendly approach to development. City politicians asked the province to preserve their Gastown heritage. The provincial government acted because, while schmoozing at art galleries doesn't move the mountains in B.C., it moves pretty much everything else. It was done and Gastown was designated a heritage area. Property owners could no longer tear down old buildings—or even significantly alter them—without permission of a Heritage Commission established to adjudicate such matters.

To the planners and developers, it was as if the gods had gotten together and changed all the rules, pulling the land out from under their grand redevelopment plans. A demolition derby, the P200 Project, is what they proposed. Tear down all the old buildings, as was the habit in those days, as witnessed by Joni Mitchell's lyrics: *They paved paradise—and put up a parkin' lot.*[6] The idea was to actually make Gastown into a parking lot servicing the rest of the downtown area! The rest of the plan was to pave a waterfront route west to the Lions Gate Bridge, cover the Strathcona neighbourhood to the south with residential high-rises, and to top it off, squeeze in a Los Angeles-style freeway east through Vancouver's history-rich Chinatown. It would have worked, too—at the expense of the area's residents who valued quality of life, community, history, and heritage.

CHANGING TIMES

The P200 project was stopped in its tracks. The people fought city hall and won! The Strathcona and Chinatown communities were saved. But in Gastown the local economy was a disaster, crime rates were rising, unemployment was sky-high, and homeless people congregated in abhorrent living conditions. Many ideas were bandied about but never gained wide agreement. Drugs, health issues, property decay, social conflicts, legal and liability issues: all led to civil confrontations over the solutions proposed. Every faction was right, of course, from their own perspective.

Many of the P200 "resistance" ringleaders became household names in Vancouver, including Art Phillips, who subsequently became mayor of Vancouver, and Mike Harcourt, who also took a turn sitting in the mayor's chair and later became the thirtieth premier of British Columbia. But not even these leading lights could build political consensus around a solution for Gastown. The provincial government had set a new direction when it designated Gastown a heritage area, but the work of making it happen would fall to the city. Unfortunately, the city was low on funds and short on answers.

Gastown property owners and merchants[7] were caught between the rocky task of making profits in a slum and the hard obligation of preserving historic character in their rundown—now heritage— properties. These challenges came devoid of any helpful solutions, handouts, or the tax incentives that since have become the norm for governments everywhere.

Could the fortunes of Gastown turn again? Had Gassy Jack not shown the way? Turning their backs on common sense, local businesses led by visionary citizens seized on the historic character of

VISIONARY LEADERS

The partners of Town Group Realty (Larry Killam, Bob Saunders, Howard Meakin, and Ian Rogers) redeveloped historic Gastown properties, including the landmark Gaoler's Mews.

With Ed Keate and the Gastown Merchants Association, they were a leading force in Gastown's rejuvenation as a vibrant people place. In 1971, their efforts resulted in approval from a penny-pinching city council (more than half the costs to be borne by a special tax on the merchants and property owners) for a $1.3 million community renewal project.

As it turned out, the penny-pinchers recouped their investment many times over, partly from the tax levy on the Gastown property owners and merchants, but vastly more from increased property valuations and tax revenues in those and subsequent years.

the area. By first recapturing old features, then adding new ones to enhance its period ambience, they set out to transform Vancouver's skiddiest row into its silkiest purse.

Local, provincial, and national governments were lobbied, again, for financial support. City planners and council members responded in a way that contributed significantly to Vancouver's growing reputation as a freethinking zone. Gradually, out of the fires of civil unrest and entrepreneurial spirit, an innovative—and ultimately award-winning—redevelopment plan was forged. Early in the 1970s a public-private urban renewal project was initiated that would add cobblestone roads, paved sidewalks, and ornamental lighting to give a classy turn-of-the-century ambiance to the streets of Gastown. With that public support, property owners, businesses, and residents focused on remaking the neighbourhood into a historic tourist attraction and trendy entertainment centre for the city.

A NEW PROBLEM

"The devil is in the details" was as true in rebuilding Gastown as in any other project. One of these details was a private project slipped smack into the middle of the redevelopment while the streets were still dug up to be resurfaced with period cobblestone-like pavers. A private utility, Central Heat Distribution Limited, realized that the Gastown renewal project would be paying to dig up Gastown's main drag, Water Street. Central Heat responded by accelerating its own construction schedule, putting in new underground steam pipes.

But buried steam pipes and connections need looking after to keep them working reliably. Technicians access the steam pipes and do their maintenance work in small—about six feet by six feet—control rooms. In a control room, the steam pipes are fitted with traps that remove hot water (condensing steam) from the line. That's a safety feature to prevent bursting pipes and worse. When the water level rises high enough in the trap, it trips a float lever. That in turn opens a valve, releasing a shot of steam that blasts the water into a drain. It's a nifty arrangement, but one that requires venting for the hot, moist air that results.

One would think that Central Heat must have communicated its construction intentions to the city, even though, as a private utility, it wasn't obliged to do so. Perhaps the information simply fell through the cracks between city departments. Whatever the reason, the Gastown project planners found out rather late; not a problem in itself, but the new control room required ventilation to keep it cool.

THE SOURCE OF THE STEAM

A large boiler plant nestles against an escarpment at the eastern edge of the downtown core, producing steam for well over a hundred and fifty major buildings in Vancouver.

To hide the necessary vents, Central Heat had a plan that could best be described as unfortunate. They used square blocks of cement to conceal their vent pipes in those days—and that *was* a problem. A modern block of unadorned cement smack in the middle of Water Street's new Edwardian streetscape would undermine the hard work and creativity that had gone into its design. It seemed a small issue, but these steam-room vents had *not* been part of the planning.

In a valiant effort to make a virtue of necessity, Central Heat hollowed out the blocks to make street planters. But heat from the escaping steam gradually killed everything planted in them with the exception of a healthy crop of cigarette filters and Styrofoam coffee cups. You can still see a few of these tree planters around the city, but thanks to Jon Ellis, not in Gastown.

Jon Ellis—City Planner

Jon Ellis and his bride were students at the University of Colorado who had a passion for skiing. Ellis, an architecture major, was told, "There are jobs-a-plenty for architects in Vancouver." So the couple's plan made itself and they followed it one, two, three: graduate, move to Vancouver, go skiing. Oh, and by the way, find Ellis a position with an architectural firm.

Vancouver had four architects for every job in the early '70s, Ellis remembers—a serious wrinkle. After three uncertain years, he traded in step four of his three-step plan for a contract with the City of Vancouver Planning Department. Initially he was to redesign Water

STEAM CHESS

The new steam line was a big project that required all the property owners along the street to put up with a steam pipe through their basement walls.

One building owner—who must have been a chess player—moved to charge rent for use of the space the pipes were to occupy in his building. His gambit was declined.

STEAM CONTROLS

Central Heat's condensation removal system and steam clock connection

UNDERGROUND STEAM

There are miles of steam pipes under the streets of Vancouver.

Street as part of the Gastown urban renewal project—a fortuitous development for the area as it turned out.

When Mike Egan, Ellis's boss in the city planning department, was promoted in 1974, Ellis eagerly applied for and won the Gastown planner position. His first assignment in the new role was to manage the reconstruction of Water Street, implementing the plan he had earlier helped to create.

Ellis had a shiny new promotion, an old rundown street to renew, a youthful desire to renew it well, and perhaps an unstated admiration for Don Quixote. And he had a windmill, the problematic vent cover practices of Central Heat.

Enclosing the vents was a good idea for safety as well as appearance. But a dreary, plant-slaying cement block decorated with a dead tree and bits of plastic would spoil the Edwardian Era ambience Ellis was tasked to create. Which raised the question, what would work better?

THE IDEA

A STEAM VENT COVER

Central Heat's standard covering for control-room air vents looked remarkably like a blocky cement planter, because that's what it was.

Ellis started at the source. He explained his problem to the people at Central Heat, asking if they would make a change given the circumstances. They responded with a typical abundance of bureaucratic compassion: Sorry, we can't help. No one he approached would consider any alternatives to the cement planter.

So Ellis went to the top. Appealing to the company's president, Jim Barnes, he met a kinder reception. This is the point where the idea of a steam-powered device really started to gather, well, steam. Barnes was action-oriented and liked the idea of showcasing his hot product in some way, while contributing to the new Gastown ambience. That was encouraging, so Ellis went to see Director of City Planning Ray Spaxman.

A visionary advocate of citizen involvement, Spaxman is a giant in the modern history of Vancouver's community development. Director of Planning from 1973 until 1990, he led Vancouver out of regulations-bound constraints that seemed to pound every design idea and property development into a common shape, and shifted the focus toward people, emphasizing environment and neighbourhood. He was instrumental in giving citizens access to the planning process through local area planning committees and representation on the city's development permit board.[8]

After hearing Ellis's account of the steam vent problem, the inappropriate and ineffective planter-box solution, and Jim Barnes's enthusiasm, Spaxman—who Ellis says "always seemed to have a pencil in his hand"—suggested a steam-powered sculpture and began sketching what to Ellis looked like an upside-down baby's mobile. "Interesting notion," said Ellis, thinking that using the steam was good, but as an Edwardian architectural option a street mobile was on a par with the plant-killer. However, Ellis chose not to argue for other alternatives, taking this approval-in-principle as sufficient for his purposes.

As he left Spaxman's office, Ellis cogitated on how to hide the steam vents without spoiling his streetscape … *What kinds of things did they put on the best street corners in Edwardian England? There were street lamps for sure, maybe ornate gas lights, and street clocks were popular. Could the vents be hidden in the base of a street clock? Steam power was big in Edwardian England. Why not a steam-powered clock?*

There were many reasons *why not*, as it turned out, and Spaxman's idea undoubtedly would have developed into a noteworthy artifact; but it didn't happen. Innocence and ignorance played a blissful role in the events that followed, and how Ellis finally got his steam clock adds a fascinating subplot to the story of Gastown's redevelopment.

"TIME AND STEAM DON'T MIX GOODBYE!"

A loud *click* echoed in Ellis's ear!

Ellis was optimistic when he started looking for a quote to build a steam clock. A quote should be no problem; there are lots of … hold on! Who builds big clocks and knows enough about mechanics to create one that uses steam? Like a budding telemarketer, Ellis hauled out the Yellow Pages and started dialing.

The clockmakers he called wouldn't even talk to him. "Clocks and steam don't mix. We're not interested," was all he heard—an attitude that would dog the project to the end. If Ellis failed to leap this early hurdle, he would save himself a lot of effort: winning approval from the city's senior managers; wheedling money from Gastown property owners and merchants; motivating city hall politicians, with visions of votes perhaps, if the idea of making history didn't fire them up. And he would avoid the stress of finding funds for this unplanned and unbudgeted clock.

Too, the project would require an unusual combination of skills. Finding someone able to build it would be like looking for the proverbial needle. With established clockmakers so unwilling, Ellis was feeling as if the clock industry was entirely the wrong haystack.

Maybe it was time to give up on the idea. It was a small addition to Vancouver's award-winning urban renewal of the Gastown historic

REBUILDING A STREET
The steam pipes run under the sidewalk.

WATER STREET RENEWED
Waiting for the steam clock

area. Ray Spaxman's steam-driven mobile idea could be developed, or perhaps that nice, steam-heated aquarium someone had suggested.

But! Ellis's imagination didn't want to quit on the steam clock idea. It seemed more practical and would add to the desired Edwardian street ambience while concealing the pesky vent pipes already sticking out of the sidewalk. Yet time was flying by and the steam clock idea would too unless a way could soon be found to make it happen.

In frustration, Ellis hoofed it over to have a talk with his boss, Mike Egan. "For the life of me I can't understand why, but the people who should know say it can't be done," Ellis exclaimed.

Egan empathized. He also thought the clock idea had merit. As they discussed Ellis's difficulty, a couple of unrelated items came together in Egan's mind. *I read an article about a sculptor and clock collector here in Vancouver. Now where was that?* After some suspenseful minutes, Egan recalled that the article had been in a local newspaper, maybe the *Province*.

Thanks to a skilled librarian at the Vancouver Public Library, the article was found in less than an hour. Reporter Nicole Strickland's

THE CONNECTING PIECE

A newspaper article led Jon Ellis to the man he needed to find.

TIMES PAST PRESERVED IN COLLECTION OF TIMEPIECES

BY
NICOLE STRICKLAND

Ray Saunders is a man with time on his hands.

"Not enough time," says Saunders, who is a part-time horologist — one who tinkers with timepieces. Of the pocket watch he is holding, he says "It takes a full day just to clean one of these. This is a time consuming hobby."

Saunders, of 1650 West Thirteenth, collects, repairs and restores antique watches and clocks. He owns about 180 antique watches, and estimates his collection of old clocks to number 75.

"I began collecting when I was given a box of old watches which were in umpteen pieces. After I had assembled and fixed them, I suddenly found I owned a couple of very rare watches.

"By sheer luck one of those first watches was a minute repeater made in 1850. That means it chimed the hour, and then the quarters, and then the number of minutes past the quarter.

"It's a self-winding watch —rare in those days—with a calendar and a beautiful gold hunter's case, which encloses the whole watch. It's a chronograph, too—a stopwatch—and was specially manufactured in Vancouver for Mr. T. Fleishmann.

See here? His name is inscribed on the dial.

"Well, that got me interested in reading all about the history of watches and clocks, and before I knew it, I was a dyed-in-the-wool horologist."

Saunders' specialty is antique clocks, because they can be displayed easily and increase in value at about 15 per cent per year. He says "I write a little history about each timepiece in my collection, to make the hobby more interesting to others who aren't horologists."

One of the most interesting clocks Saunders has repaired was an antique grandfather clock valued at $9,000.

"It wasn't striking quite right. The butterfly fan inside was slipping to slow down the striking mechanism and it was going bongbongbong. . . bong . . . bongg. . . bonngg . . .

"It had nine different bells and one big bell for the chime, as well as nine hands: three to record the hours, minutes, and seconds, one to point out the signs of the zodiac, a hand at the top which pointed to the phases of the moon, a hand showing how many days into the phases of the moon one was, as well as hands pointing to the months, days, and the position of the sun. One hand even showed how much time was left on the weights

before the clock needed winding.

"I guess the clock was about 1790 vintage. It had a very ornate case with a raised Chinese motif. Everything worked via the main drive mechanism. It was the most accurate clock I've ever seen.

"I couldn't move one of its hands without all the other hands moving, though, so I had to disconnect the dials of the clock just to check the strike. It even had a 24-hour dial instead of the standard 12-hour dial. It was a lovely thing."

Some grandfather clocks,

KEN OAKES PHOTO

RAY SAUNDERS . . . and part of his collection

Saunders comments, have little rocking ships that sway as the clock ticks. Some have little cupids that strike the hour. But if the style of clocks and watches has changed today, so has the workmanship and the amount of time spent in making each timepiece.

"In the old days a watchmaker could work a whole year in his spare time to make a fantastically beautiful and accurate watch. The competition was fierce.

"Today, unless you pay a stiff price for it, the average watch isn't as well made as the watches of the past," says Saunders. "The coming thing in the next 10 years is electronic, rather than mechanical watches. The electronic watch hums and doesn't have a balance wheel.

"And the watch repairer will be a thing of the past. Today the jeweller is limited to the number of watches he can repair daily; in the future, working with electronic watches, he'll put a whole new plastic pack assembly of parts into a broken watch, rather than having to take the whole thing apart."

Saunders is a former jeweller himself, and says that most people know little about watches.

"When I repaired watches for a living, one chap who came in said he thought we cleaned them by dunking them in gasoline and twirl-

ing them around on a string."

There are no parts available for fixing antique watches, so Saunders either makes the part himself or robs another watch from the stock of old watches he keeps.

And then occasionally Saunders comes to grips with a problem that faces many would-be repairers of watches: "Sometimes I put a very complicated watch together and find I have two screws left over. I don't know where they belong, but the watch works perfectly."

If you're looking for something really different and unique for yourself, or a gift, call in to the Sculpture Studio on W. Georgia, and see the intriguing time-pieces of sculptural horologist, Raymond Saunders.

Ray's years of horological experience (clock making) when welded with his sculptural talent produce useful and fascinating artistic works which can best be described as 'future time'.

The price of time, a la Saunders, is extremely inexpensive, the clocks, a combination of intricate mechanical parts, assorted metals and old clock gears, range from $95 to $500.

One of the 'custom specials' should you so require, is the indexing of the clocks in the language of your choice.

human interest piece labelled a local artist who made clock sculptures as "a man with time on his hands." It read, "Call in to the Sculpture Studio on W. Georgia, and see the intriguing time-pieces of sculptor and horologist, Raymond Saunders."

Eureka! Ellis thought.

"I am looking for someone to build a steam street clock. Can you do it?"

This is the essence of the phone call Ray Saunders, struggling clock expert and budding time artist, received from Jon Ellis in August of 1974. "You bet! Let's meet and discuss details," said Ray Saunders's empty wallet. And the Gastown Steam Clock story began.

Can You Build a Steam Clock?

At their first meeting, Ellis sought assurances: "Are you sure you can build a steam clock?"

An accurate answer would have been, *I have no idea*, but Saunders, struggling to make ends meet and already enamoured of the idea of a paying clock project, thought a simpler response would work better. "Yes," he said.

With hope rising, Ellis asked, "How much will it cost?"

As *I don't have a clue* passed through his mind, a less complex $25,000 passed out of Saunders's mouth. (*I could buy an airplane for that amount.*)

Excited, Ellis asked the make-or-break qualifier: "Can you do it by September 1975?"

The answer was, *not a prayer*. But why confuse communications with such a petty technical detail? Saunders reduced his answer to a simple yes. (*Maybe I can figure a way ...*)

Ellis, thinking of all the naysayers he had encountered and perhaps feeling a touch triumphant, said, "Send me a proposal."

Saunders, already counting chickens, or golden geese, replied with a customarily cautious OK.

Ellis recalls thinking, *he either really knows what he's doing or he is guessing wildly*.

Of course, neither Ellis nor Saunders recalls the conversation word for word, but the gist of it and surrounding events is accurate as presented here—and don't you love it when a plan comes together?

And so Ellis hooked up Saunders, the man with the right mix of knowledge, skills, and overconfidence, with Jim Barnes, the action-oriented president, to work out the steamy details. They hit it off and Barnes became a stalwart supporter, committing Central Heat

PLAYING THE GAME

Gastown's property owners and developers joined with local merchants to populate the city's committees and added their own complement of committees and subcommittees to do the work and get things done.

Membership on the many Gastown committees often overlapped. Jon Ellis became a member of at least a dozen, often as the chairman.

These committees became the means by which Ellis, with Killam, Keane, and their supporters, influenced city hall and satisfied or bypassed in-built bureaucratic resistance, eventually to award-winning acclaim.

to providing steam for the clock and maintaining the connection indefinitely—for free.

Meanwhile, Ellis moved on to the next hurdle: bringing the Gastown property owners onside.

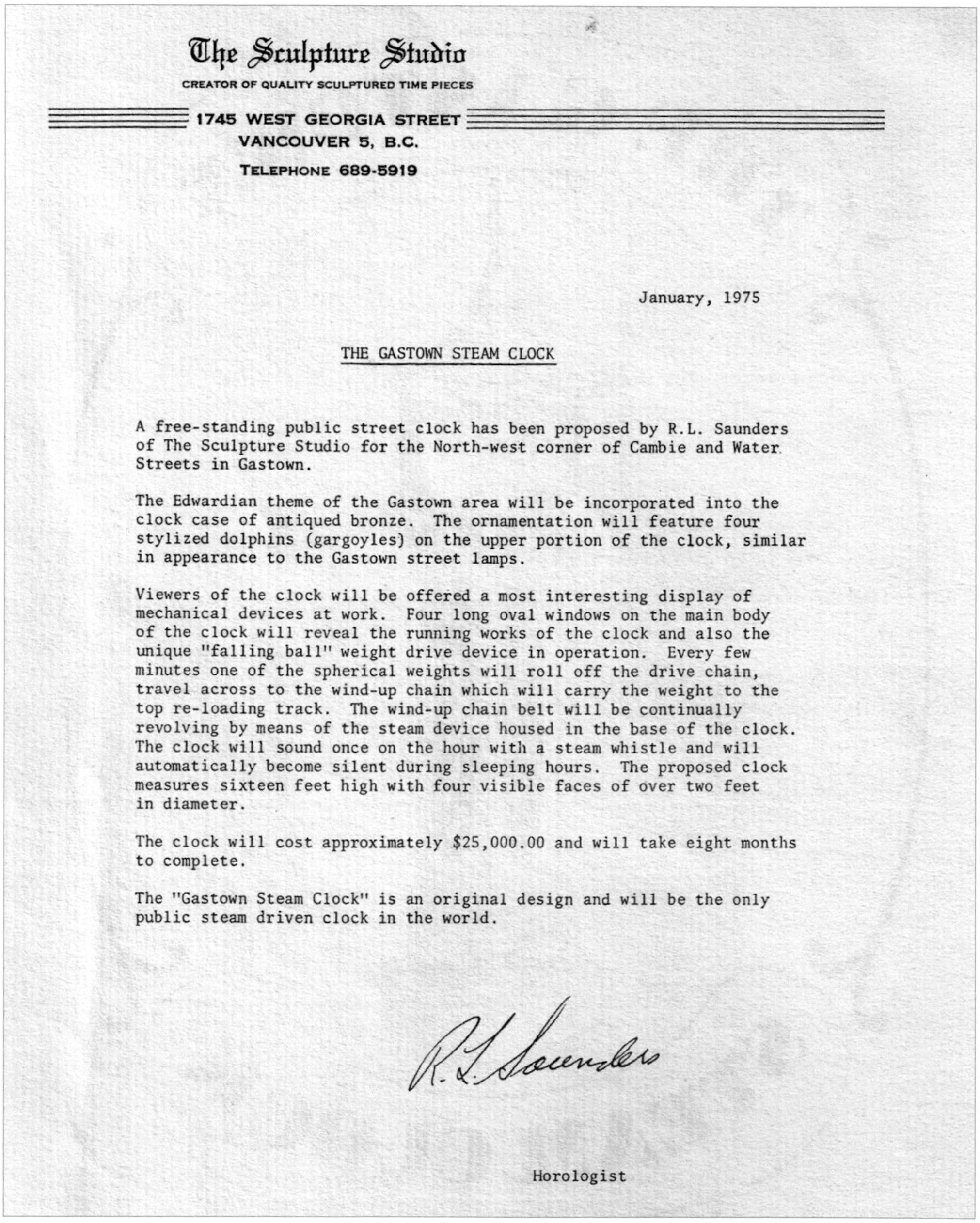

The Sculpture Studio
CREATOR OF QUALITY SCULPTURED TIME PIECES

1745 WEST GEORGIA STREET
VANCOUVER 5, B.C.
TELEPHONE 689-5919

January, 1975

THE GASTOWN STEAM CLOCK

A free-standing public street clock has been proposed by R.L. Saunders of The Sculpture Studio for the North-west corner of Cambie and Water Streets in Gastown.

The Edwardian theme of the Gastown area will be incorporated into the clock case of antiqued bronze. The ornamentation will feature four stylized dolphins (gargoyles) on the upper portion of the clock, similar in appearance to the Gastown street lamps.

Viewers of the clock will be offered a most interesting display of mechanical devices at work. Four long oval windows on the main body of the clock will reveal the running works of the clock and also the unique "falling ball" weight drive device in operation. Every few minutes one of the spherical weights will roll off the drive chain, travel across to the wind-up chain which will carry the weight to the top re-loading track. The wind-up chain belt will be continually revolving by means of the steam device housed in the base of the clock. The clock will sound once on the hour with a steam whistle and will automatically become silent during sleeping hours. The proposed clock measures sixteen feet high with four visible faces of over two feet in diameter.

The clock will cost approximately $25,000.00 and will take eight months to complete.

The "Gastown Steam Clock" is an original design and will be the only public steam driven clock in the world.

R.L. Saunders

Horologist

THE COVER LETTER
The original proposal specified dolphin gargoyles—that could not work as whistles.

THE PLAN

Ellis knew the city would not fund a steam clock. At the time, the city had formed a citizens' committee of property owners, the Townsite Committee as it was known, to assist in the process of planning Gastown's future. The day after Saunders gave his assurances, Ellis presented the idea and the cost to the property owners at a meeting of the Townsite Committee. He wondered if they would like it and, more importantly, if they would pay for it.

The steam clock would help improve the area and that could only be good for business, went the logic. Naturally, being the most likely to benefit, property owners and merchants were the prime candidates for donations. So bringing them onside meant not just building consensus for a steam clock agreement, but also raiding their pockets for some serious change.

Ellis must have made a good impression, because they immediately adopted the steam clock idea. Moreover, concrete support was forthcoming. John Parker of Pacific Rim Distributors in Gastown, and chairman of the Townsite Committee, wrote a cheque on the spot for $2,500—ten per cent of the quoted cost. Very quickly, $10,000 was pledged and commitments made to raise the balance.

Vision, know-how, steam, financial capital … all the ingredients were in the mix. It looked like there was nothing left but to shake and pour. Except they weren't in Gassy Jack's informal saloon; they were in a ponderous bureaucracy. For a combination of perfectly legitimate and perfectly bureaucratic reasons, Ellis needed a proposal in writing.

ORIGINAL PROPOSAL
The proposal title-page graphics were a tad primitive but got the message across.

THE OFFICIAL PROPOSAL

The initial quote was not much more than an educated guess. Saunders was blowing smoke (*the Gastown Smoke Clock?*) but Ellis wanted this clock, so he chose to believe. However, smoke signals were not good enough for conducting city business. For the city's bureaucrats and councillors, the proposition had to be more substantial. This was getting serious, so Saunders called out for help.

By virtue of having his own lathe in a work area next to his bedroom, Saunders had excelled in his metalworking class at Vancouver Technical School. His relationship with his instructor Doug Smith grew into a personal friendship after Smith discovered Saunders's knowledge of antique timepieces. Saunders was invited into Smith's home to teach the teacher.

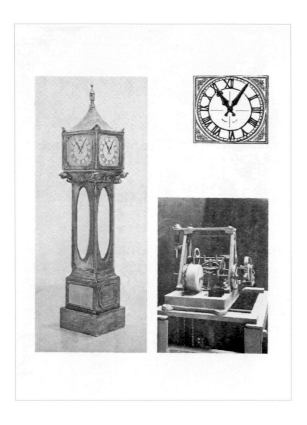

```
Basic Costs of Gastown Steam Clock

Submitted - January 1975
            By: R. L. Saunders

1.  Four way Clock Work and Movement
    complete                              $  3,400.00

2.  Four Clock Dials Complete               1,500.00

3.  Main Framing and Raw Bronze
    for Case                                2,700.00

4.  Winding and Weight Devices              1,600.00

5.  Steam Device and Fittings              3,000.00

6.  Contingency Costs                      3,500.00

7.  Labor, Design, Moulding and
    Associated Engineering                 9,300.00

                                        $ 25,000.00
```

THE BUDGET

Creativity wins out over realism.

PROPOSAL GRAPHICS

Images of the first model,
clock face, and movement

Not surprisingly, years later when Jon Ellis requested a steam clock proposal, it was to Smith that Saunders turned. Even the most fearless risk-takers have mentors, especially risk-takers who live to tell about it. Saunders ensured his survival by partnering up with Smith to design and construct the clock. But first they needed preliminary drawings and a cost estimate in writing.

Working to Ellis's specifications, they began melding city structural requirements and the physical constraints imposed by the location with Edwardian design principles, Saunders's artistic horological vision, and Smith's experience.

Saunders also called in his artist friend Jonathan Blackshaw to create presentation materials. Blackshaw was "a good old English bloke," according to Saunders, "and a very good artist" who later became a movie set designer. He lived on a boat in nearby Coal Harbour. Blackshaw turned Saunders's concept sketches into coloured illustrations.

The illustrations were rendered with tea ink on clear acetate sheets. Saunders recalls Blackshaw boiling tea down to make the ink. Laying them over a watercolour background drawing (also created by Blackshaw) of the site as it was expected to look after being renovated gave the team a good idea of how the alternative designs would appear when installed on the street corner.

Blackshaw not only drew those first images, but also built scale models of the clock: the first, about a foot high, came complete with ugly gargoyles. The second, a modified concept, replaced gargoyles with steam whistles. The models brought the clock to life at the planning meetings, lending solidity to their otherwise vaporous imaginings.

With the steam clock proposal in process, it was time for Ellis to take on the bureaucracy.

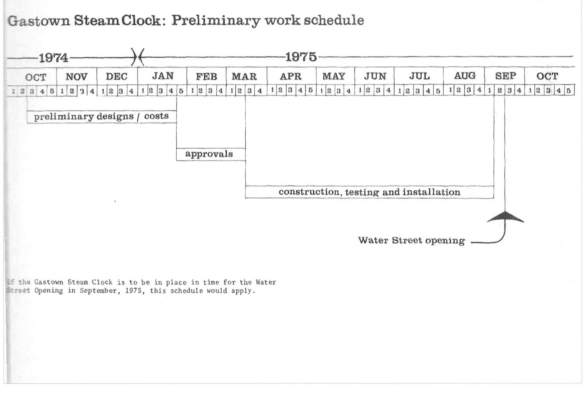

THE ORIGINAL TIMELINE
Planning is everything; the plan itself means nothing.

City Hall

Sidewalks are a city responsibility, so a street clock, of steam or any other persuasion, placed on a city sidewalk would best be given into the city's keeping. But underlying the tight-fisted stewardship of Vancouver's bureaucracy were layers of policies and rigid regulations designed to manage resources and minimize legal risks: not the stuff of ingenuity and invention, as anyone who has ever tried to implement change through a committee will attest.

That presented Ellis with another challenge: how to get Vancouver's council to break a heretofore inviolate rule, a rule that precluded the city from accepting gifts of mechanical devices and the ongoing cost of maintenance that inevitably accompanied them. A steam clock would be, without doubt, just such a mechanical device. One can imagine a skeptical chorus of harrumphs along with assertions that ponderous bureaucratic procedures would stop this steam clock Jon-foolery.

Would Ellis succeed in winning official acceptance, or would bureaucratic chill cool the steam of bubbling enthusiasm and stop the project cold? Compounding the problem was the perception that this had to be decided—right now. As it turned out, there was some spare time, about three years of it, but they didn't know that then.

Ellis was an innocent in those days, a junior bureaucrat and fairly recent immigrant from the United States. He knew little of Canada's version of getting-things-done-through-government. So, doing what Americans do best, he innocently democratized the internal workings of the city government in his pursuit of steam-driven street art. Ellis built direct relationships inside the Vancouver administration and with the city's councillors.

Which all seems to make sense—but was strictly verboten at the time. The bureaucracy took a dim view of such proceedings and would have quashed them with vigour. Only, no one told Jon Ellis. So, like a spy in their midst, he quickly learned who made the decisions. All unknown to his superiors, he brought the city's managers and politicians onside with the clock idea.

In the 1960s and '70s, Vancouver's mayor and council relied very heavily on the city manager's recommendations when it came to spending or initiating change. Fritz Bowers was city manager and Ken Dobell was his deputy. It's probably accurate to say that Ellis's style of communication helped build good working relationships with both men.

When Ellis brought his arguments for a steam clock to Dobell and Bowers, his proposal earned a positive recommendation in the city manager's report to council.

Ellis had also developed good communications with members of city council like May Brown, who was, amongst her other duties, responsible for Gastown liaison. Brown sponsored the proposal to council. The finished proposal included a cover letter and was only four pages long, including the title page. It was straight-to-the-point simple and not fancy, yet it earned sober consideration from city

THE THREE JO(H)NS

Jonathan Blackshaw (behind the pendulum), with Jon Ellis (left) and John Parker (right)

councillors. Sober consideration in this case meant that serious objections were raised regarding budget and liability implications.

In response to the councillors' concerns, capital costs were promised by the Gastown merchants and property owners while the steam supply, with all steam maintenance costs, was pledged by Central Heat. These assurances, along with Ellis's guileless but very effective behind-the-scenes manoeuvres, were enough to overcome the opposition. For the first and as far as we know only time, the city accepted a gift of a mechanical device—and city council approved the steam clock proposal.

While moving the project over Vancouver's administrative hurdles, Ellis was resourceful—and obviously annoying to the distressed department heads. Ellis wasn't trying to be a rebel; he was simply doing a job the best he could. The story of how he accomplished this is a fine example of a classic political end run. Ellis insists it wasn't done on purpose: "I thought I was just doing my job. I didn't know the

A FIFTH COLUMN

Jon Ellis facetiously called Ken Dobell his "deep mole" in the city's administrative hierarchy. Dobell's ability to get things done in a bureaucratic maze subsequently earned him a position as British Columbia's Deputy to the Premier and Secretary to the Privy Council.

City Planning   *Piswo*

February 5, 1975

MEMORANDUM TO   :   M. Egan

CC. TO   :   J. Gift-Ellis

RE   :   Steam Clock

Thanks for sending me (I guess you did) information on steam clock.

I am sorry to report that I am very disappointed with the designs - an Edwardian theme.

I have never liked reproduction stuff, let alone concerned with new ideas. As a consequence I feel that at least to me, the clock looks daft. I come from the school of thought that believes the best design of today lives better with the best design of other ages, rather than design attempting to copy features of the past.

I guess it's all gone too far now to discuss this profitably.

R.J. Spaxman

RJS:hs

TOO LATE TO SAY NO

Director of City Planning Ray Spaxman is not happy with the period design.

proper bureaucratic procedures." And maybe he was blind-as-a-bat lucky, as he (mostly) avoided confrontation with senior management. Whether impudent or innocent, you have to love Ellis's abundant store of self-esteem.

Now they had a project with a challenge; no, two challenges: they had a first-ever clock to build, and equally importantly, they had to establish good accounting procedures to manage the many thousands in donation dollars they were expecting to come pouring in. Ellis already had a good start on the fundraising with support from Jim Barnes and Central Heat and from John Parker and the Townsite Committee. Now he needed another $15,000. In 1974, that was a whack of dough.

FUNDING FUNDAMENTALS

PLEASE HELP!
Fundraising for the steam clock was very slow after the first round.

Fundraising was looking like a summer breeze after the first presentation to the Townsite Committee generated on the spot the cheque from Chairman John Parker for ten per cent of the expected project cost. But few "big" donations followed, although some small amounts were promised, an omen of what lay ahead.

Another committee was formed. The Gastown Steam Clock Fundraising Committee was established to seek donations and to set up and manage a Gastown Steam Clock Fund.[9] Co-chaired by Parker and James Pollock, a Gastown merchant and member of the Gastown Lions Club, the committee's initial target was, naturally, the $25,000 proposed to city council, which amount Saunders had pulled out of his hat sans benefit of hard quotes from suppliers. The committee canvassed for cash contributions.

The Gastown Lions Club became a hotbed for raising steam clock money. Club member and super-dedicated fundraiser Pollock, doing most of the leg work, accosted his fellow merchants and property owners and other interested individuals and businesses. But getting new donations was like squeezing water out of rocks. So they got innovative, promoting a variety of events and special programs, mostly legal, to separate the unwary from their spare cash.

Says Saunders, "We all asked, what can we do together as a group?"

RUSHING FOR GOLD

They decided on a casino night. This ultimate fundraiser was going to leave the project rolling in dough. But it was hard for people (meaning potential sponsors) to picture the clock—not surprising as they had nothing to compare it to. Something they could see, a display of the envisioned end product, was needed.

Saunders remembers calling on the artistic talents of his friend Jonathan Blackshaw once more. Blackshaw painted the spare, full-size clock layout drawing (they had made two on Doug Smith's rec room floor, just in case), turning it into a life-size poster. Saunders still has that painting (all sixteen feet of it) rolled up in his workshop.

Held just days from the original deadline of September 21, 1975, for installing the clock, the event was billed as the *First Annual Gold Rush Casino*, and the life-size steam clock poster decorated the wall. A gala dress-up event, run by the Gastown Lions Club under the auspices of the Gastown Historic Society, it was the peak of fundraising activities and by all accounts a great party. It served a good cause and was harmless fun, yet strictly speaking it was a criminal enterprise.

The volunteer fundraisers licensed a bingo lottery, which was lawful, but ran a set of games which, one gathers, stretched the bounds of 1975 legality. This event may have marked the start of a trend that eventually led to the expansion of legal gambling in B.C., now the principal source of funds for many of British Columbia's not-for-profit organizations and charities.

A Claim Jumped

But even though it was well attended and a tour de force in the Gastown social scene, the *First* (and only) *Annual Gold Rush Casino* was a near bust financially. It was unfortunate, but a big chunk of the take from the casino night flowed right back out again.

"We thought this casino night would solve all [the fundraising] problems," says Saunders. "Things went wrong there. After all the work that went into that casino night, it only raised a few thousand dollars."

The Vegas professional brought in to run the event assured them, based on the turnout, number of tables, and duration and stakes of the games, that they should have grossed $30,000. After checking with every dealer at every table, that estimate was confirmed as fairly accurate. Curiously, the profits that should have been left in the till failed to remain there: the take was roughly one-tenth of the expected amount.

The gambling organizers, to pull off this nefarious deed without going to jail, had talked unofficially to officials who "know nothing about illegal casinos, but what you do is mumble, mumble, and then you mumble," and that's how you make an illegal casino-night-that-never-happened. Since the casino night never happened, the

THE FOUNDATION GROWS WEEDS

... while the steam clock fundraising committee tries to grow dollars.

THE GOLD RUSH CASINO

The first annual casino night— and the last annual casino night— with a full-size painted drawing of the steam clock behind the partygoers.

organizers could hardly call in the police when most of the profit they didn't make wasn't turned in.

Someone (who was not in charge of the money that was not there) insisted, when questioned, that there was only a small (non-existent) profit from the casino-night-that-never-happened. He later was reported to have found his way to Mexico, perhaps with the missing not-money from that non-happening.

DESPERATE MEASURES

The faster the budget grew (ultimately reaching almost three times the original estimate), the slower contributions became. As the flow of funds slowed so too did progress on the clock falter. Money supply soon became so critical that Saunders had to max out his own credit. The fundraising committee was reduced to borrowing the money for their precarious venture.

The project stretched into 1976 and then 1977 as the swelling budget absorbed a trickle of donations. "We were desperate," Saunders said. "We had a very good president [of the Lions Club] at the time, Doug Piepgrass, who had some very good ideas with the Habitat Dollar and then the Gastown Indian [Trading] Dollar programs; they raised a lot." Taking the form of souvenir dollar coins, the Habitat and Trading Dollars were legal tender and could actually be used for purchases, but only in Gastown. Of course, the more coins kept as souvenirs, the greater the profit for the fundraisers.

The Lions Club even resorted to selling Gastown shopping bags. But it wasn't enough. Instead of rolling in dough as originally expected, the steam clock project was left wallowing in debt, and the fundraisers were left at a loss as to what they could do that would work. So Parker and Pollock and their committee continued digging for gold in a played-out claim.

But back in the spring of 1975, the original budget amount had been raised or promised and these fundraising uncertainties and challenges were still in the future; the ponderous power structure in Vancouver's departmentalized bureaucracy had been bypassed, and the project had received the approval of Vancouver City Council. The mantle of leadership passed from Jon Ellis to Ray Saunders, and the focus of steam clock activity moved to Saunders and his crew of volunteering employees, friends, and the other helpers dished up from time to time by a benevolent universe.

HABITAT DOLLARS

Habitat Dollars were made legal tender in the city during the program. It was a highly successful promotion, raising thousands of dollars for the Vancouver Gastown Lions Club and leading to the idea of a Gastown Trading Dollars program for steam clock fundraising.

GASTOWN TRADING DOLLARS

Gastown Trading Dollars, a set of coins featuring famous B.C. native chiefs, were legal tender in Gastown. Although not as lucrative as Habitat Dollars, they contributed to the $10,000 the Lions Club donated to the steam clock fund.

A QUESTION OF INNOCENCE

In the early summer of 1975, they were still innocents, with a lot of questions and no answers. Could the clock be built on budget? Would Saunders find a way to make the steam work? Would the fundraising committee collect the promised money? Would Saunders get cash when he needed it? Could the September 1975 target date be met for the scheduled Grand Opening of Gastown and the clock's unveiling ceremony?

An eclectic array of bizarre barriers yet lay ahead on the path to a working steam clock: more "clocks and steam don't mix" attitude, naval bronze waves, steam engines on steroids, low ceilings and numb fingers, clock-parts ransom demands, a tune machine timing mystery, and bothersome bathroom urges.

This record of adversity, disappointment, and delay raises the question, how did the Gastown Steam Clock manage to get itself built at all? The answer turns out to be obvious …

Ignorance is bliss.

A NOT-QUITE-NORMAL MIX: A NOTE ABOUT RAY SAUNDERS

Did Ray Saunders's skydiving and scuba diving play a role in creating the world's first functional public steam clock? Might not a lifetime of risk-taking, along with an expectation of getting away with it, been pivotal? What none can doubt is that Saunders's practical education and enthusiasm for metalworking, his many years as a watch and clock repair technician and estimator, and his penchant for antique clock collecting contributed directly to the project's ultimate success.

Saunders's risk-taking bent showed up in his entrepreneurial decision to become an artist. He expanded his metalworking and design horizons into metal sculptures comprising old clock parts. Now there's an artistic pursuit that at first blush would appear guaranteed to keep "starving" in the job description. Yet many of Saunders's creations are gorgeous and captivating.

In 1976, shortly after being commissioned to build the steam clock, Saunders opened his own studio, Creative Metal Sculpture, locating at 141 Water Street. At $600 a month for the main floor plus only $200 a month for a 3,000-square-foot basement, his costs were a far cry from today's premium rates for trendy Gastown premises. He maintained a shop in Gastown for the next twenty-five years.

SAUNDERS'S CLOCKS
A hobby grows into an avocation and then into a career.

Saunders spent every spare minute and every not-so-spare dollar finishing the steam clock in a workshop he set up in the basement. Meanwhile, the Creative Metal Sculpture Gallery, with two full-time and several part-time employees, struggled to make a go of it, barely providing Saunders with a hand-to-mouth living, a practice he never strays too far from even today.

Saunders's independent spirit, positive attitude, and unusual array of talent and skills meshed with the imaginative, can-do attitude of city planner Jon Ellis in the social, political, and economic maelstrom of Gastown in the 1970s. Looking back at the people and circumstances, it seems a working steam clock was almost inevitable.

All this is rather humble stuff. Yet Ray Saunders is arguably the most widely known horologist in B.C. if not Canada. Over the years his passion for time machinery developed from a minor watch collecting hobby to a job, a local business, and finally an international reputation, with well over a hundred public clocks, including six steam clocks and one more in the works, to his credit. The first of these was the Gastown Steam Clock.

SAUNDERS WITH STEAM CLOCK MODEL

Making a model is one thing. From his expression in the photo, Saunders was starting to realize how different building the full-sized working steam clock would prove to be.

OF MEN
AND
MONEY

A PRECARIOUS BUSINESS

The Creative Metal Sculpture Gallery on Water Street is open for business—and Saunders incorporates the Gastown Steam Clock Company Limited to make it official. Saunders and crew install a new sign.

OF MEN AND MONEY

Innocence doesn't hold you back. With the funding offensive being mounted by valiant volunteers, Ray Saunders and Doug Smith turned their attention to the nitty-gritty of design refinements and clock manufacturing.

The objective was to design a steam clock that would contribute to Gastown's planned turn-of-the-century ambience. The original specifications focused on street sightline and liability, as well as concern for the safety of admirers and passersby. It had to be noticeable and situated on a street corner, which meant being pretty big—for a clock. At the same time it had to be small enough to leave pedestrians and power lines unimpeded, and with the heat and moist air ventilating through it, it had to be waterproof inside and out. The design, while satisfying the new Water Street aesthetics, was to include a visible interior of sufficient interest to engage people's attention and curiosity. Saunders remembers designing it to be "comprehensible."

FROM CONCEPT TO REALITY

The official mandate—worked out by Jon Ellis and Saunders with Mike Egan as early as August 1974 and subsequently—called for the design and construction of a "notable and entertaining" street clock. Flying in the face of conventional wisdom, it was to be the world's first-ever street clock to showcase steam. The specifications called for "steam whistles" as chimes to be heard for "two city blocks" but no farther, and to "automatically turn off for the sleeping hours." It was to have "four dials" (facing four directions) in a "four-sided case," with "visible clock workings" in the waist of the clock, a "steam powered drive"; and of course it was to provide "discreet ventilation" for the steam control room located underneath.

Add a load limit for the foundation of twenty tons, which the clock wouldn't come close to weighing, and that was about it. This left a lot of room for creativity. Saunders's imagination worked overtime to create a larger vision—one of a triumphant piece of working art that would fascinate throngs of clock-watchers in every particular: a unique drive mechanism to deliver power to the hands of the clock, bullet-proof glass panels, a steam engine, ingenious lift and drive chains, a gold-plated pendulum bob, and other curiosities of design and function.

BUILDING A STEAM CLOCK
Doug Smith, Charlie Mackenzie, and Ray Saunders, hard at work

DESIGN MODEL #2

Jonathan Blackshaw made this second concept model after the original design turned out to use some unworkable assumptions— like wide-open dolphin mouths for steam whistle openings that could not toot.

CHIME CHOICE

Britain's Big Ben spread the fame of "The Westminster Chimes" tune. It was the tune selected in 1859 for the Clock Tower in the Houses of Parliament in London.

As the hour is struck on the famous old bell after the four 4-note phrases of "The Westminster Chimes" have been played on the smaller bells, so too does the steamboat whistle following the tune whistles on the Gastown Steam Clock.

In retrospect, this was a pretty tall order. And Saunders was to accomplish it all in roughly half a year on a budget of $25,000! On the plus side, the mandate came with a commitment of steam connections and steam supply, promises for almost half the estimated cost, and a committee to raise the remaining funds. You could forgive everyone for thinking this would be a cakewalk: a few more weeks of fundraising games and the cash would be in the bank. Then, a few months of hard work by Saunders and his team and the clock would be on the corner. Completing this project looked to be as easy as blowing a whistle!

But hold on! What Saunders didn't have would fill a longer list. There were no detailed drawings or finished design; no clock mechanism; no steam engine or steam whistles; no clock case, face, numerals, or dials. There was no place to build it, available tools were rudimentary, and the specifications were mostly guesswork. Yet, with such a challenging list of uncertainties, Saunders was still eager.

THE FIRST ORDER OF BUSINESS

Doug Smith played a key role once again. His friendship, knowledge, and resources were instrumental in the initial stages of the project. Smith didn't have all the answers, but he knew where to look. It was through his local network and connections—to machine shops, foundries, teachers, tradesmen—that many steam clock suppliers and willing helpers were found.

Along with his machining skills and industry connections, Smith brought his own rec room (where much initial planning and drawing work was done) and his home workshop (where many of the clock parts were manufactured in the first year) into the project.

Smith wanted to do a full-size drawing to scale—to generate specifications and a list of parts and to work out the details. He pulled huge, 16-by-3-foot sheets of paper from somewhere, and with his wife's permission and a bunch of pencils, he and Saunders repaired to the rec room. Smith's rec room had square, 12-inch black and white tiles that served nicely as a giant drafting board.

They used up three erasers before they were finished, but they got it done. It was from this drawing that they expected to take the measurements for everything that was to go on, in, or under the finished steam clock, to be sure it would all fit. And they made the extra "in case" copy that was subsequently painted by Jonathan Blackshaw and used as a poster at the big casino night fundraiser.

Saunders and Smith, like a pair of coordinated steam pistons, powered forward. Saunders conceived an inventive endless-loop chain with spherical weights that would drive the clock by the force of gravity. To prove out the concept, Smith designed and built a model of the ball drive mechanism. It actually worked to a point and was a great toy (no steam required; it used a hand crank). The final version of the drive was considerably modified by Saunders in the final months of testing and assembly, but the basic concept and structure survived to become one of the most intriguing aspects of the steam clock.

It also exemplifies the rewards of friendly cooperation. But money-trouble loomed, the curse of relationships of every kind.

A Rising Budget

With finances so tight, Saunders often made do with materials on hand from his gallery. And costs would have been even greater if he had included the cost of the basement workshop set up to make and store the clock structure and components. Labour, skilled and otherwise, donated over the three-year life of the project by friends and others caught up in the vision also helped to keep the costs down. Still, an innovative and unique construct doesn't come cheap, even in the 1970s, especially one that takes three years to design and build using trial and error or, as Saunders calls it, "Burt's method."[1]

Saunders's desk sagged as the price quotes came thudding down. Even as the first 25,000 donated dollars accumulated, it became apparent that some of the costs in the projected budget were gravely underestimated. The bills piled up as Saunders ordered more parts and materials.

"The big shocker was the cost to cast the bronze clock case: $22,000!" exclaims Saunders. "This was the lowest quote and the big wake-up call." A base cube, bottom cube, top cube, three side panels, and front door panel were all to be cast in bronze. Casting metal is a lengthy process requiring such nitty as the coefficient of contraction for naval bronze and the gritty of a mould that had to be slightly oversized to allow for shrinkage when the liquid bronze cooled.

Looking for ways to cut costs, Smith made a deal with a foundry, Pacific Bronze Co. Ltd., to cast the bronze case parts for $3.50 a pound. The idea was to buy unfinished castings for the waist panels and base cubes and to spend time and effort, in lieu of dollars, to get them smoothed and polished. The cheapest unfinished bronze castings still consumed $13,122 of the original budget, plus taxes.

NOISE SPECIFICATION
Even after the steam pressure was reduced, the whistles were too loud to let run through the night.

DRAWING TO MEASURE
Saunders says he never used the full-scale drawing to take measurements, implying it was of limited use. Could that have something to do with the many "fit" problems he experienced installing the clock?

WHERE TO START

First, they needed someone to build wood patterns of each section of the clock case to make moulds. Smith hooked another of Saunders's old teachers on the idea. J. L. (Len) Thorson[2] was Saunders's cabinet-making instructor from his Vancouver Technical School days, and he proved to be the right man for Smith and Saunders to turn to. Thorson did yeoman service, building wooden patterns[3] in his home workshop at well below retail cost.

SIDE-PANEL CASTING MOULD

The white bars are for aligning the two halves and the dark bars are the flue channels.

GRINDING A SIDE PANEL

Polishing a side panel in back of the Georgia Street gallery before Saunders moved to 141 Water Street

BRONZE WAVES

When they arrived at Saunders's shop, the bronze castings were very rough and wavy. Two belt sanders and a whole lot of elbow grease later, Saunders had all the castings "as smooth as a baby's bottom."

Despite Thorson's excellent patterns, the naval bronze castings, ordered unfinished to reduce the cost, arrived in waves. The price of $3.50 a pound was a steal of a deal, but as is so often the case, the bargain turned out to be false economy. The castings were rough, and sanding them consumed an inordinate amount of time, elbow grease, and sanding belts.

A cement foundation for the clock to sit on was in place and waiting, so the next thing was a strong clock frame to attach to it. The frame would have to bear the weight of the power train, bronze cubes, and side panels; the clock workings, roof, and whistles; as well as wires, Central Heat's steam pipes, the tune machine and steam engine, and all the smaller bits. Too, it was to be out on the street in Vancouver's weather, stand as tall as two adults and a child, and as it turned out, stand up to both adults and children climbing on it. The wear and tear of time, gravity, and avian offences also were to be considered, and potential vehicular encounters should have been.

"Sturdy" seemed to be the operative requirement. The clock was going to weigh a ton and then some (two and a half tons in the end). As part of the cost control effort, Smith created a project for his Vancouver Technical School students: to build the steel frame in his metalworking shop. So Van Tech's class of 1975 got to play a role in the steam clock's creation.

ENGLISH CONNECTIONS

Smith brought in Charlie Mackenzie, a fine machinist and steam hobbyist with a well-equipped home workshop, to help with steam power. They needed to find a steam engine that would fit in the clock and still look the part. Mackenzie knew a guy who knew another guy … a lead that took them to Stuart Turner Ltd., a British maker of model steam engines.

Saunders also had to find a clock movement: the time keeping machine. A design from the Victorian or Edwardian period in English art and architecture would be perfect. Ignoring the earlier "time and steam don't mix" rejections from potential clockworks manufacturers, Saunders wrote letters that eventually led him through Murray Clock Crafts of Toronto to Gillett & Johnston of Croydon, England, makers of authentic period clockworks.

Raiding his piggy bank to buy tickets, Saunders went to England in May 1975 to see if the proposed model steam engine from Stuart Turner and clockworks from Gillett & Johnston would meet his requirements.

The sample movement shown to Saunders at Gillett & Johnston was a small church-tower clock movement installed a century before. In for cleaning and servicing from its church-tower home for the first time, it was covered with a hundred years of filth and pigeon poop.

MENTOR & STUDENT
Doug Smith (right) with Ray Saunders (pre-beard) and the steam clock frame in the Van Tech metalworking shop

GILLETT & JOHNSTON
The clockworks, original tune machine, and pendulum were all purchased from the famous Croydon foundry of Gillett & Johnston, who were proud to be "by Royal Warrant, Clockmakers and Bell Founders to H.M. King George V."

CLOCK MOVEMENT
Designed in 1875 by Gillett & Johnston of Croydon, England, the pinwheel escapement mechanism is snugged up safely between triangular clock plates.

A SENSE OF HISTORY
The Gillett & Johnston basement was full of old clock movements of all sizes, some of them huge, all salvaged and saved when replaced by newer models.

**THE QUEEN AND
THE CALENDARS**

Saunders was given a tour of
Stuart Turner's long, thin factory.
Support posts marched down the
middle, all the way to the foundry
at the far end. Saunders was
highly amused when given the
VIP treatment—sort of.

Thwap, thwap, thwap the
calendars went on one post after
another, down the full length
of the factory, to announce
the incoming VIP. The pin-up
calendars were flipped and the
side with the queen's picture
turned to face out.

STEAM POWER

This single cylinder steam engine
had no self-starting mechanism
and had to be kept running
constantly—hence the wear and
tear factor was very high.

OVERKILL?

In the customs warehouse,
Saunders couldn't tell which end
of the clock movement's shipping
container was up. About three
feet on each side, it was such a
sturdy box that it "could have
gone to Africa and back by ship."
Instead, there it sat, "beside a
pallet with delicate electronic
gear wrapped in nothing but
a bit of plastic wrap."

Yet the original bushings showed no sign of wear, a key to power use
and reliability. The lack of wear sold Saunders on the movement,
and it was "just the right size" too. Steve Coombes, Saunders's host
at Gillett & Johnston, pulled out a drawer and showed Saunders the
movement's original rice paper drawings, dated 1875!

With the clock movement lined up, Saunders turned his attention
to another key piece of the steam clock—the planned power source.
A six-month delivery queue for the desired Stuart Turner model
steam engine didn't bode well. Neither did the initial introduction to
P. N. Barnard, the manager at Stuart Turner Ltd., who couldn't place
Saunders until he said he had come from Canada. "Oh, the guy who
wrote the letter!"

During a subsequent tour of the Dickensian steam engine factory,
Saunders managed to win a new steam clock convert and cement
a business relationship. The engines showed up on Mr. Barnard's
desk before their meeting was over, and Saunders came home from
England with three Stuart Turner #4 model steam engines.

The seals and moving parts of the steam engine had to be
upgraded to run twenty-four hours a day, seven days a week. In his
home workshop, Mackenzie chromed the steam engine cylinder and
replaced both piston and seals with fluorescent plastic copies, making
the fit tighter while reducing friction, in an attempt to prevent steam
from escaping into the clock's interior.

Meanwhile, Gillett & Johnston built the clockworks and, determined that their new antique creation would come to no harm in
transit, packed it for rough weather, anticipating a journey by sea.
But, fortunately for their promised delivery date, it was not too large,
as they feared it might be, to go by air cargo. Saunders's employee
and clock volunteer Mike Spence was in awe as he deconstructed the
complex shipping crate and freed the delicate mechanism inside.
The weight and quantity of nails fastening the wood crate ought to
have prevented the plane from lifting. In spite of all that effort, there
was some shipping damage. Gillett & Johnston's Steve Coombes
wrote that he gave the shipping company's representative a tongue-
lashing and elicited a "strong verbal apology."

A SPACE FOR TIME

Creative constraints imposed by Saunders's business partner had
already strained the working relationship at their shared Georgia
Street gallery. In the summer of 1976 (Saunders missed the original
deadline—and many others), when the opportunity arose to rent a
Water Street retail space that included a large basement, Saunders

jumped. He started a new business, the Creative Metal Sculpture Gallery, and set up shop in Gastown. It was a risk, but with the help of the expected steam clock revenues, he thought he could make it.

In his new digs, Saunders busily turned the long basement under his street-level art gallery into a series of display, storage, and work areas for manufacturing smaller parts and to assemble and test the steam clock. Overcoming layout limitations, power problems, heating hardships, and a drippy drain in the new location involved innovations as simple as a length of rope tied to a pipe and as easy as running an extension cord next door. Other changes were more complicated—like subdividing the basement and replacing a fire exit stairwell with a stepladder.

The clock was to be 16 feet high, but the basement ceiling could only muster up 10 feet of clearance! Six vertical feet of challenge—what to do? The ceiling would not move. Saunders could not make the clock any shorter. It was already a concession to make it "only" 16 feet tall. Something had to give.

SAUNDERS, MACKENZIE AND SMITH

The clock takes shape.

LOTS OF ROOM(S)

From lounge to display room to finishing workshop to grinding and sanding area to cutting and bending area to, behind the doorway at the back, the steam clock assembly workshop

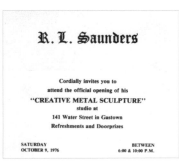

THE INVITATION

Saunders throws a party.

STAIRWELL MANUFACTORY

The clock frame acquires its bronze skin in the stairwell.

How about building the clock in two pieces? The final testing could be done after the two parts were installed on the cement base patiently waiting on the corner. Or maybe build it lying down? Or … look at that back stairwell! It must be 20 feet high— and 20 feet is more than 16 feet. The answer was to remove the back staircase and assemble the steam clock in the two-storey opening left behind.

Saunders doesn't remember whose idea that was, but it was a good one. Of course there were other challenges, but this solution really started the ball rolling. After all, there was another stairway at the front of the basement and the back stairs would fit, nice and snug, leaned against the furnace-oil tank at the back. Besides, it was only going to be for a few months, right?

So the back stairs (and the fire escape route for the building) were removed for the duration of the project and a ladder attached to the wall in lieu. The back door was locked so no one would fall down the open stairwell (or escape a fire if …) and assembly of the steam clock began. His landlord might have objected more strenuously about the fire escape if there had been any hint it would be gone for three times Saunders's promise of a "maximum six months."

BUILDING A DREAM

Being a "first ever" endeavour, building the clock was a big job and offered roomy accommodation for devilish details. Nothing much worked the first time—or as expected. Burt's method became a standard operating procedure. Grandfather clock proportions and unworkable ideas bowed before engineering specifications and physical realities. And strange things happened.

WHEN NATURE CALLS

BURT'S METHOD IN ACTION

Saunders gets a little behind in his work–two years of behind before unveiling day finally arrived.

Sometimes, when Saunders went into the basement to work on the clock, his work was interrupted by abnormally frequent calls from nature. An undesired side effect of these frequent calls was disruption to his train of thought, focus, and concentration, slowing the clock's progress. The natural urges seemed to peak every time it rained— a common occurrence in British Columbia that keeps the place green. One day, Saunders connected a couple of seemingly unrelated bits of information.

As we all know, the sound of running water magnifies the bladder urge. And secondly, every time it rained for more than a few minutes, a sound, very like that of a horse answering nature's call, echoed through Saunders's basement workshop. Not a genteel image, but the way Saunders expressed it was rather less delicate. The sound level varied according to the amount of rain, but was always there in the background.

As it turned out, the building's rain gutters drained to the rear of the Creative Metal Sculpture Gallery's basement, falling three feet from the end of the drain pipe and splashing into a sump, creating the sound effect. Saunders thought to hang a rope from the end of the drain pipe into the sump. The water trickled down so quietly that he claims a full percentage point gain in clock-building productivity from that one little innovation.

Breaking and Borrowing

The cash flow slowed to a cash trickle even as, inexorably, costs expanded beyond the original off-the-top $25,000 budget. In the spirit of shameless begging, taken to a whole new level by Jim Pollock and the Gastown Steam Clock Fundraising Committee, Saunders resorted to borrowing things.

For example, his landlord neglected to pay the building's furnace fuel bill and the fuel ran out. Extension cords snaked all over from the building next door (same owner) to little effect, circuits constantly blowing when heaters were attached. Saunders, luckier than most of the tenants, had an alternative source of winter heat. Central Heat's main steam pipe passed through his workshop. "Every winter (even after the clock was finished) the insulation fell off and in the summer it would go back on again," Saunders confesses.

Being constantly short of funds diverted some construction effort, and the shrunken cash flow led to other problems. Doug Smith lost faith in the outcome. Smith held brass whistles and decorations (parts that he had made) to ransom, refusing to hand them over until he was paid for his work. With no cash on hand, Saunders put his antique watch collection into Smith's keeping in exchange for the parts. Smith got impatient and threatened to sell the collection. The fundraising committee borrowed $15,000 from the Royal Bank to keep the project going and eventually to pay Smith. Saunders's watches were returned, but Smith left the project and their relationship withered and died.

Happily, there were some budget benefactors who helped to ease the monetary misery. Woodward's Stores, Saunders's former employer, was the third largest donor to the clock fund. In addition, the downtown store dedicated a prime window display for several months to promote the steam clock unveiling ceremony.

A DRAIN ROPE FAQ

The rope, for the detail-oriented reader, was left over from some camping adventure. It was made of jute, and it was still performing its assigned task admirably until the building was renovated years after Saunders had moved to 123 Cambie Street.

CURRENT PRICES

To put the steam clock costs into a modern perspective, the bronze castings, duplicated from the Gastown Steam Clock drawings for Otaru, Japan, in 1990, cost $75,000. At 2010 prices, the steam clock would likely cost in the neighbourhood of $350,000-$450,000.

THE CAT IS OUT OF THE SACK

Woodward's Department Store makes it public in their prime display window—there's no backing out now.

DOES IT FIT?

Saunders measures tune machine clearances.

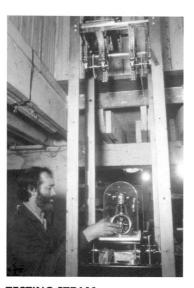

TESTING STEAM

The glass globe steamed up, obscuring the engine; it never got out of the shop.

DOES IT WORK?

Saunders tests the chain and bucket drive system.

THE PARTS GO ON

Saunders starts installing the falling-ball gravity drive system.

Bill Woodruff, store manager of Woodward's, participated on the Gastown Historic Committee. Saunders says, "Whenever we needed to move something heavy, for fundraising events or in the workshop, we went to Woodward's. They even loaned me a pallet lifter and told me to keep it as long as I needed." It was needed many times over many years.

Parts and Men Are Tested

As time flew by, a myriad of length, width, height, and positioning issues were resolved. At last, Saunders spaced the bearings along the chains. The drive chain only needed three weights to keep moving, so there was extra capacity. Imagine the anxiety in the shop as Saunders gave the pendulum a swing to set the mechanism in motion. Here was the acid test of their unorthodox vision, eclectic design, jerry-rigs, and repeated applications of Burt's method. And it worked—like a charm!

Or was that like a hex? Had they actually built a real time machine by accident? The clock seemed to be travelling back in time. Never mind! Not even the counter-clockwise motion of the hands could dampen their joy. They would reverse the planet's spin, if necessary. Fortunately, a simpler solution was available.

THE TOP CUBE

Saunders installs the hands. No wonder it ran backwards—he has it upside down!

TIME FLIES—BACKWARDS?

Mike Spence and Margie Meinzinger look on while Saunders figures out how to get time flowing forward again.

ALL THAT'S GOLD GLITTERS

Jonathan Blackshaw adds 24k finishing touches to the clock face.

"I got the assembly reverse-mounted in the frame," Saunders realized, with a sigh of relief. After carefully removing and re-installing the drive mechanism, time resumed its forward march.

It was actually running—what a rush! A bit of the bubbly and a toast shared by Saunders and his staff seemed appropriate. Saunders formally presented the clock to his staff along with a detailed explanation of the unique lift- and drive-chain mechanisms. A mood of confidence and optimism infused the Creative Metal Sculpture crew.

So the works worked and the hard part was done. Or was it? They had a steam system to install, a case to assemble, and the shiny decorative bits to finish. There was still a ton of work to do.

The drive mechanism, for example, had to deliver reliable power to the lacquered hickory rod and seventy-five pound, gold-plated pendulum bob. From there power would go through a pinwheel escape mechanism to drive the cogs that turn the wheels that power the axles that move the clock hands.

Making all that work reliably was a tall order—they had to test things out constantly. Saunders says, "With, I would say, thirty days before the clock was to be unveiled, I decided to try out the motor system on the tune machine [also brought from England]. The motor just sort of quivered—it didn't even turn around." Saunders had missed seeing the plate on the electric motor that said fifty-cycle. North American current is sixty-cycle.

The tune machine's job was to regulate the timing and duration of steam delivered to the whistles, creating "The Westminster Chimes" tune on the hour and the quarter hour. It had to work, but it couldn't.

THE CREATIVE METAL SCULPTURE GALLERY CREW

Margie, Susie, Mike, Ray, and George celebrate with a bottle of bubbly on the occasion of the first successful trial of the clockworks working (backwards).

HOT WORK

Saunders and Johnny Podlesnick of Central Heat test the steam whistles at the Central Heat maintenance shop.

ABOUT CYCLES AND SECONDS

Remember your high school electricity lessons about direct current and alternating current? Most of our motors and lights run on alternating current, which means the direction electrons flow is reversed many times every second. In North America, the standard frequency is 60 times per second. In Europe, it's 50 times per second.

The European tune machine motor, built for 50-cycle operation, needs 1/50th of a second of current to get moving—1/60th of a second just doesn't do the job.

Saunders was so desperate he would even have read the instructions—but there weren't any. The tune machine had a three-position pulley giving three speed settings, so trial and error was effective for selecting the correct speed, in England, and not a scrap of documentation had come with the supplied motor. Saunders needed to find a sixty-cycle motor to run the tune machine tunefully.

When you're not looking, it's so easy to find things. But, with a specific item in mind, even when you know it's out there, nothing! Saunders ran all over town desperately searching for an electric motor that would play the tunes properly. He was offered motors with rheostats (for controlling the turning speed), but they were all too large to fit in the space available in the clock case. It seemed there was not an appropriately compact variable-speed motor to be had at any price. With just two weeks to the unveiling deadline, "I even bought a used

BALL AND CHAIN

Saunders had to redesign the ring bucket mechanism to get the balls to load and unload reliably.

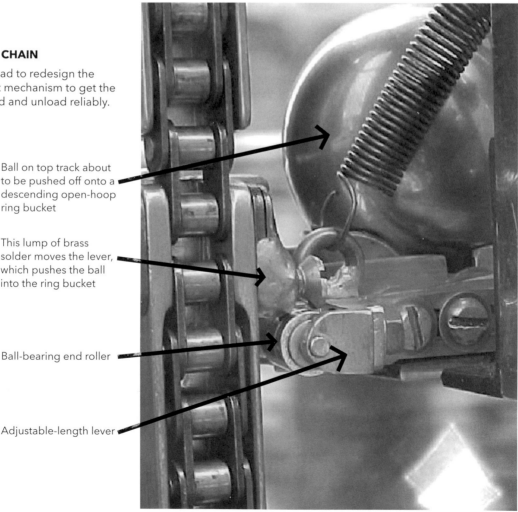

Ball on top track about to be pushed off onto a descending open-hoop ring bucket

This lump of brass solder moves the lever, which pushes the ball into the ring bucket

Ball-bearing end roller

Adjustable-length lever

sewing machine motor with a foot pedal on it, a nice machine but it went way too fast." With the luxury of hindsight, many possibilities for finding or figuring out the right speed come to mind. It is a measure of their stress that none occurred to anyone.

With no solution in sight, Saunders turned his attention to a different problem. Drilling and tapping (making and threading holes) to attach the bronze cover plates and doors to the steel frame was a major clockmaking activity. In the final weeks, more brass sheets and rods were purchased, measured, cut, and fastened. Nuts, bolts, washers, and screws also had to be found. Difficult problems arose in the first attempts to line up the holes. To help in the process Saunders purchased a variable-speed electric drill, and that gave him an idea.

"I had this Black & Decker drill, so I hooked that up to the tune machine. I could adjust the speed control on the trigger, and that ran just perfectly. I made some clamps, clamped that thing in there, didn't even know what speed it was going ... but it worked!" (This drill solution worked for more than eleven years, before being replaced by a proper motor.)

"The stressful part in July and August [1977]," says Saunders, "was making the pieces for the ball loading and unloading levers. Smith's idea was there, in that he had made a little model work, but the size of levers—there were no drawings; nothing was calculated." Saunders had to make it up as he went along. "It was stressful to try and make it all work and have it completed enough that I felt comfortable taking it all apart again" to be installed on the street.

Support from Unexpected Quarters

The funding battles went right down to the wire. With only two months to the September 24, 1977, unveiling deadline, Saunders needed some $2,000 to complete the plaques and buy materials for the clock. The fundraising committee had already dished out every donated dollar and the project was well beyond the enlarged budget of $42,000. Saunders had to plead and cajole: "It's not going to work if you don't do something."

After some heated words Ellis and John Parker, steam clock enthusiast, first donor, and enthusiastic chair of the Townsite Committee, laid down the law, and Saunders had to eat some time. The new understanding included late delivery penalties Saunders would have to pay if he missed the deadline. On these conditions, the fundraising committee borrowed again so Saunders could finish the job.

THE VARIABLE-SPEED DRILL
Saunders solves the 50-cycle tune machine motor problem with the variable-speed hand drill he had used to drill holes in the case and frame.

TESTING THE WHISTLES

Whistle testing looked to be a high hurdle. Accessing the steam control room wasn't practical and would give the show away. Yet, they needed to be sure that the tune machine would play and the whistles would work. Jim Barnes stepped up again, allowing Saunders access to Central Heat's boiler-plant maintenance facilities. Saunders attached the whistles to the roof assembly, and with help from Central Heat's maintenance crew, the whistles were tested. Even though they had to wear hearing protection to test, this was accomplished with no one realizing how loud they would be on the street.

A VEIL FOR UNVEILING

It's hard to unveil something that isn't veiled to start. No veil, no unveiling; no unveiling, no drama. A rather large cover was required. Even if it had been in the budget, it wouldn't have helped. By the summer of 1977, all the donations were spent and then some. And Saunders's pockets, while not full of holes, might as well have been. The loyal sponsors and donors were tapped out. The steam clock needed a gift horse.

Fortunately, a husband and wife team, Roy and Dorothy Pegler, heard of the situation. The couple manufactured a fashion line titled Elizabeth Gordon. Their factory sat kitty-corner to the clock at the intersection of Cambie and Water Streets (below Townline Sportswear, of which more later). The Peglers, being familiar with clothes horses, were confident they could handle the job.

"Roy and Dorothy were wonderful, giving people," Saunders recalled. "Many good deeds can be laid at their doorstep. Roy was also a founding member of the Gastown Lions Club. Their Granville Street retail outlet was a bit risqué," he added.

Their specialty store on downtown Granville Street drew people with great self-esteem and a sense of bedventure. Roy and Dorothy manufactured underwear—diaphanous lingerie in fact, some of it quite shameless. They also had no shame when it came to self-promotion. Being innovative, and clearly possessed of fast reflexes, they offered to be the gift horse, promising to supply a veil to cover the entire sixteen feet of clock. And they came through! These generous folks custom-designed, custom-made, and personally donated the urgently needed veil—hopefully not too diaphanous—just days before the celebration.

BALLOONING BUDGETS

Saunders requested the budget be raised from the overly optimistic $25,000 figure, at first to a paltry $42,000. The final cost was a bit over $54,000, or $58,000, or $67,000, depending on which report you quote.

TIME TO GIVE UP?

Saunders tries the hoist on for fit and comfort. Is he just horsing around or secretly thinking about giving up?

ANOTHER BRIGHT SPOT

B.C. Bearing Engineers made, among other things, ball bearings for machinery of all shapes and sizes—including bearings for the revolving base of construction cranes. When the steam clock was just about ready for them, Saunders ordered a dozen one-pound ball bearings.

By this time, the steam clock had enjoyed a considerable amount of notice in the local press. The owner of B.C. Bearings, Wendy Macdonald, had apparently been intrigued by the whole steam clock idea. One day, Saunders realized that he had not received an invoice for the ball bearings. Upon inquiring, he was told, "Consider them our contribution to the steam clock."

The timing was fortuitous. Saunders says, "It was a nice gesture and really encouraged me."

WHISTLE WHILE YOU WORK

The main steam whistle, a "bull whistle" that was to provide a loooong-toot climax to the hour chiming, had yet to be made. And it looked like the big whistle would fall prey to the ongoing funding shortages. But Charlie Mackenzie knew Tom Hobbis and Tom Hobbis was the brother of Cap Hobbis, a great friend of Gastown in the early days, and Tom had a collection of whistles. Before you knew it, Tom Hobbis offered to bring the original whistle from the S.S. *Naramata*[4] steam tug out of retirement so it could assume time-telling duties perched at the pinnacle of the steam clock's roof. Saunders accepted with alacrity.[5]

In the last few weeks before the September 24, 1977, unveiling deadline, Saunders acquired missing pieces and applied Burt's method with a vengeance. After almost three years of effort with nothing to show for it but a bunch of pieces and parts, monumental money troubles, deadline pressures, lost friendships, startling protests, and frustrating delays, all of a sudden, it seemed, the steam clock was together—just in the nick of time—and the almost-on-schedule unveiling went ahead without a hitch. Well, maybe with a couple of hitches.

Three, actually, including the unveiling cord problem, the unexpected veil enhancement, and the big embarrass-moment.

THE VEIL'S ON TIME
The veil conceals all but the roof and whistles as the hoarding comes down.

THE SS *NARAMATA*
On the beach in Penticton, B.C., the SS *Naramata*, sans steam whistle, is being restored by the SS *Sicamous* Restoration Society.

STEAM CLOCK TOOLS

The Gastown Steam Clock, much like the human body, comprises more than two hundred major parts and a time-consuming list of itty bitty bits.

In addition to the time works, there are the frame and bronze cubes and glass panels and the steam engine and electric motors and steam pipes and a tune machine; there are clock faces and hands and numbers and a pendulum with a bob and a time-rating nut; there are brass plates and decorative bits and a copper roof with steam whistles and bronze gutters.

All by itself, the lift- and drive-chain assembly has sixty-eight component parts. And there are a cement foundation and steam fittings and electrical wiring and metal brackets and fasteners—and the list goes on. While the steam clock is astoundingly complex, the tools Saunders used to make and assemble the clock comprise a surprisingly short list. Notable were:

THE METALWORKING LATHE

YE OLDE LATHE

As of 2011, it was pushing seventy-five years and still running like a top. (Or, as Saunders says, "It runs like a lathe.")

Years before Saunders's birth, his father had purchased an old, heavy metalworking lathe from the B.C. Equipment Company. When the family moved to Vancouver from Courtenay in 1957, Mr. Saunders said to his son, "If you pay all the moving costs, it's yours."

Saunders accepted the challenge. He took a weekend job as a handyman and general factotum at the D. L. Morris Furniture Company. He dusted furniture, swept floors, and counted dirty dishes returned from wedding rentals (a company side-business); and he made the money. For the princely sum of $75, Saunders barged his bargain across Georgia Strait from Courtenay to its new home in a Kerrisdale basement. A pretty good deal for a teenager.

A Cataract Bench Lathe made by Hardinge Bros. of Chicago, Illinois, it was one of the primary tools used to build the steam clock. With it, Saunders manufactured, resized, or reshaped many of the rods, wheels, and more arcane round bits that hold the workings in place and make them go around. He even polished the whistles on the lathe, using emery cloth to clean off the lacquer that over time burned dark from the heat of the steam—until the decision to stop fussing and let them age.

BENCH DRILL PRESS

Every screw- and bolt-hole in every piece of brass, every bracket, everything except the main steel frame was made on this bench drill press. And Saunders damascened—a swirling finish like a Damascus sword—all the internal brass clock pieces on it as well. He used a piece of an old, oak baseball-bat handle as the dowel for the buffing spindles (more cost savings) and oil with "#80 grit" (like black sand) to make all the swirl effects.

A ROCKWELL BELT SANDER

At first blush, a galumphing big electric belt sander doesn't appear useful for making clock parts. But when the clock is a sixteen-footer and the clock-case castings come looking like a bronze replica of a storm at sea, a sander of this size, belted for bronze, comes into its own. The belt sander and its replacement (the first one wore out) did yeoman service.

A BOSCH MINI-GRINDER

The mini-grinder was one of the most used tools. It made things fit, smoothed welds, and did just about everything needed to polish the surface of metal parts in preparation for lacquering. Saunders claims the case "looked like gold" in the workshop, before they sent the bronze cubes and panels for sandblasting, antiquing, and lacquering to Ornamental Bronze, the foundry Saunders also used to make the steam clock plaques (and for many other clock projects since then).

A PORTABLE BLOCK-AND-TACKLE RIG

A portable block-and-tackle assembly was pressed into service for building the clock. It had four pulleys on top, four on the bottom, and a nylon rope in between, and was used to lift the heavier components in the workshop stairwell assembly area. "It was awkward, but it worked," says Saunders.

WELDING EQUIPMENT

High-quality Smith-brand oxyacetylene torches were used to weld brass, bronze, and steel pieces, and to make parts. Saunders also had a new welding productivity tool: an automatic speed fluxer. This handy gadget sped the welding process. It made the brass flow smoothly

A HOMEMADE DRILL PRESS

The drill press itself, along with a drill press vise attachment, was homemade by Saunders—with the help of his $75 lathe. As his grade twelve class project at Vancouver Technical School in 1959/60, it earned him an A+ for the course. Along with the lathe, that drill press resides in Saunders's workshop today. Now fifty years old, it still has the original motor—which was used when purchased. Saunders says, "It's just nicely broken in." They should make kitchen appliances like that!

A STURDY TOOL AND LIGHT FINGERS

A sturdy tool and no doubt still in use by we-don't-know-who, the mini-grinder was stolen. Saunders bought a replacement, which still gets lots of use on all his clock projects. In fact, thirty-three years later, he still has hundreds of grinding discs first used on the steam clock and used on new clock projects ever since.

HUNTING AND CLOCKS ARE SIMILAR BECAUSE?

Used to hoist cubes into place inside the workshop stairwell, the block-and-tackle assembly was intended for hunters—for hoisting the animal to skin and dress, or to haul it onto a waiting vehicle. This assembly was purchased at an Army & Navy store that still operates at the edge of Gastown.

A WELDING WONDER

Eddy McAfee, Saunders's nephew, borrowed the automatic speed fluxer to show his metalworking teacher at BCIT, who had never seen one; it was leading-edge welding technology at the time. Saunders still uses it today.

TO GROOVE–OR NOT

In using round files, there's a trick to keeping the file from making grooves in the metal piece you are filing. It needs the addition of a twist or rolling motion during the stroke action. Who knew?

THAT BURT GUY AGAIN

Properly hinged and latched as originally intended, the bronze Sponsor Plaque was completed and installed as a permanent service door replacing the four Allen key bolts. It had a levered arm latch, accessible only through the main glass door, which is secured by two Abloy burglar-proof locks.

After a new (and oversized) electrical panel was installed, the new latch stopped working. The Allen key was almost called back into service, but Saunders managed to narrow the latch so it would miss the electrical panel housing and still catch.

with no oxidation by bubbling flux into the acetylene gas. It lubricates the weld without putting flux directly on the material, ensuring secure and attractive welds.

BLACK & DECKER ELECTRIC DRILL

First used to drill screw- and bolt-holes into the steel frame, then for five years it drove the tune machine that played "The Westminster Chimes" on the steam whistles.

About ten years and two variable-speed drills later, one of Saunders's Central Heat technician buddies brought over an automotive timing gun to point at the drill as it spun through its routine. It was turning at exactly 80 rpm. Saunders found a 60-cycle Bodine gear motor at Armature Electric in Vancouver that ran at 80 rpm and would fit in the clock with the tune machine. Soon, Saunders installed the Bodine motor. Exit the Black & Decker drill.

Unfortunately, the Bodine motor went out of production. When it wore out, around 2003, Saunders had to rebuild it, putting the clock out of action for three days. So, in October of 2006, the tune machine and electric motor were both replaced by a programmable electronic Omron tune control system.

The electric drill was more fun.

A MISCELLANY OF SMALL TOOLS

There were, of necessity, the usual array of measuring devices, grippers, clamps, wrenches, blunt force persuaders, and the like, items essential to any manufacturing process. For example, a variety of round taper files received a lot of use. The smaller sizes of round taper files are referred to as rattail files, because of their strong resemblance to a rat's posterior appendage.

AN ALLEN KEY

Used to lock and unlock the "temporary" aluminum Sponsor Plaque functioning as the service door in the clock base, this little tool played a "key" role during the unveiling ceremony. The plaque was only a quarter of an inch thick, so there wasn't much thread, and that stripped over the years. A nut welded to the back of the panel got it working again.

The Allen key was retired, after twenty-five years of service, when the bronze Sponsor Plaque was installed at last.

DARK TIME

Early September rains washed the summer from Vancouver's streets while Saunders disassembled the clock in the workshop and wrapped boxes of parts and large pieces of the clock in plastic. With everything ready to go, he had plenty of time to reassemble it on site before the scheduled opening ceremony.

They waited for the rain to stop. And waited.

In the end, Mike Spence, George Webster, the street musicians from California, Mark and John, and Saunders bruted it all from the basement up a long flight of stairs to the street. Ignoring the rain, they rolled everything to the waiting construction hoarding on dollies and a hand truck (borrowed from the nearby Woodward's store), stuffing clock frame, case, roof, and all the innards in like leftovers in a refrigerator.

With the unveiling just days away, Saunders, Spence, and Webster started to put the clock together. "We built the clock using Burt's method." says Saunders. "You jerry-rig it; make it work. Then come back and fix it up later." Talk about working in the dark. To compound the challenge, much of the clock was assembled at night.

Something poetic about all that, don't you think …

From innocent beginnings
a know-nothing start,
not one body knew
what they were about.
Not one body knew
how new
the workings would be,
or who would pay.
Enslaved by the thing;
not one body knew
how long this would take,
to make.
Or even if it would last,
be a legacy, or
a power symbol
for dream chasing.
Men worked in the dark, after dark,
like those doing crime.
Yet, no body knew aught,
not even the time.

Poetry aside, don't you love it when a plan finally comes together?

MUSICIAN JOHN LEADS THE CHARGE

And a bemused George Webster hangs on tight.

UNVEILING
THE VISION

POLITICAL PUFFERY

The dignitaries address the assembled multitudes blissfully unaware of the imminent arrival of Murphy with his Law.

UNVEILING THE VISION

Ahand dolly was borrowed. Packaging, tools, materials, and fasteners were assembled. A plan was made and volunteers were lined up. At long last they were ready to install the clock—and they had time to spare. There would be no more missed deadlines. "We had it apart at least three weeks ahead of when we were going to put it up," Saunders says.

Have you ever tried to keep a big present a secret? How do you hide it? How do you wrap it? And if it's a sixteen-foot, two-and-a-half-ton steam clock, on a busy street corner, how do you avoid giving away the surprise? A well-established construction practice, implemented with a twist, offered the solution: build a hoarding (a temporary wooden fence around a building or structure under construction or repair) at the construction site and make it high enough to completely conceal the structure.

The twist: omit the windows customarily installed for the benefit of aspiring sidewalk superintendents. But they couldn't block the sidewalk entirely, even though the hoarding had to be sixteen feet high. It also had to be simple and easy to make—and cheap.

With those constraints, the hoarding designed itself: take standard four-by-eight sheets of plywood, lay sideways four high, and fasten together on a frame of two-by-fours. Repeat four times—perfect.

FROM WORKSHOP TO WORKSITE

On September 7, with seventeen days to go, wood was purchased from Beaver Lumber. Mike Spence and fellow gallery artist George Webster built the hoarding in the alley to the west of Saunders's gallery, providing a percussive counterpoint to the strings of a hammered dulcimer,[1] a guitar, and the voices of Mark and John, two street musicians visiting from California. The alley was a great venue for street entertainers, except for the lack of a public facility. Saunders welcomed the duo into his gallery's washroom, winning them over as volunteers to the clock cause in the process. They delayed their return to California for a week to see the clock installed.

Two weeks before the scheduled unveiling, if you were strolling down Water Street, you would have been intrigued by the sight of Spence, Webster, and the California Duo trundling the hoarding down the street, one side panel at a time. The front end was embraced by two of the brawny volunteers, and sixteen feet later, the other end of the side panel was snuggled onto a borrowed hand dolly

THE PARTS ARE READY TO GO

Assembled and ready to wrap in plastic for transportation to the assembly site

THE CALIFORNIA CONNECTION

"They were excellent," said Ray, speaking of two Californian street musicians who made their way to Vancouver in the summer of 1977. Mark and John regaled passersby by combining the sounds of a hammered dulcimer and a guitar.

They helped carry clock–case parts, roof, and innards from Saunders's basement studio up a long flight of stairs and down to the construction site in the rain.

MUSICIANS PLAY THE HOARDING

Mark the dulcimer player helps Spence push, and John the guitar player helps George Webster balance the load as they move the hoarding sides to the site.

where two more unpaid musclemen strained to keep it upright while guiding it in the right direction.

Moving the eight-by-sixteen-foot panels was precarious work, as was raising the three sides around the weed-covered base and installing the fourth, the door side, onto its hinges. The hoarding proved to be a tight fit on the inside, which created its own set of challenges during the clock installation. But it was functional and suitably sized for the sidewalk location. Good enough! The how-do-you-hide-it question was resolved. They were almost there, almost home free. Nothing could go wrong, right?

GOING FOR IT

Much of B.C.'s sunshine arrives incognito, concealed as raindrops. As wet sunshine poured outside, inside the workshop the clock was being prepared. From the tiniest nut to the twelve-foot steel frame, to get the pieces and parts to the site where and when they were needed, it all had to be staged—and it all had to be dry.

Related parts were grouped and packaged in clear plastic wrap to make them easy to transport, and easy to find. Then, ready to go, everything just sat there encased in plastic, waiting for the weather to get better, dry sunshine being preferred for clock building.

A week went by. Something had to be done, but what? They waited, first through the weekend, then all day Monday, then all day Tuesday. With just days to the scheduled unveiling at high noon on Saturday, September 24, 1977, the steam clock was nowhere to be seen. The pieces were still in Saunders's basement workshop up the street, waiting to be moved to the site.

What if the rain doesn't stop? A sheet of plastic stapled across the top of the hoarding would make for a quick and easy waterproof cover, it was thought. It worked—at first. That the roof would have to be unstapled on installation day was irrelevant. "The most stressful thing was watching the clock and the time going by and seeing how little time we had left," Saunders recalls.

Wednesday morning, Saunders, Spence, Webster, and the California Duo started moving. Rain or no rain, time could not be stopped. The first challenge was extracting the now bare, but still heavy, steel frame from its home in the draughty stairwell while avoiding damage to the doorway, the frame, and Saunders's and his helpers' backs. With equal measures of positive thinking and proper posture, they dragged the frame out through the back elevator door and wrapped it in plastic. The ubiquitous hand dolly again proved

COGITATION
Spence and Saunders figure how to haul the frame out of the narrow basement stairwell.

its worth; backs were spared as the frame rolled down the alley and around to the construction site in a breeze.

Did that stairwell ever look bare! With nothing but ghost-like footprints in paint overspray to mark where the clock had been growing for a year and a half, Saunders waited while his emotions sorted themselves.

FINAL ASSEMBLY, FINALLY?

Workspace was cramped inside the hoarding. The largest parts, like the base cubes and frame, had to be attached to the cement base before the next pieces could be brought in. First the bronze base cube was lifted, at risk to groin and limb, and placed over the cement foundation block, now devoid of its weeds. The base cube was then secured into the cement with bolts—even a car crash wouldn't knock it loose.

Next, the whole north side of the hoarding was swung open on its sixteen feet of hinges. The frame for the clock was raised through the hoarding door next to the base. Slowly, carefully, the waist of the clock rose into position, all bolted into place while balancing on the bronze base cube—a prestidigious feat. Add-ons clung like amorous attachments as cove pieces and the plaques cube were slid into place and side panels secured.

Parts and tools were muscled from Saunders's basement studio up a long flight of stairs to the street. Big pieces went onto the dolly. Smaller parts, bits, and tools travelled in a shopping-cart-come-tool-buggy, one of the many to be found in Gastown's back alleys. And all was rolled down to the construction site with rain still shining down and everything wrapped like leftovers from the fridge. Keeping it all dry was a finicky business. Too finicky in the end: boxes of small parts and fasteners, stacked against the inside of the hoarding, filled with water. "It kind of broke my heart to see everything getting wet," said Saunders.

Gassy Jack put up his saloon in twenty-four hours, with volunteer labour, using a barrel of whiskey to motivate and fuel the crew. We still have twenty-eight hours, thought Saunders; maybe beer will suffice. Beer was obtained.

Wheeling parts around to the construction site was "a piece of cake," said Saunders. Assembling it was more like eating spaghetti with a single chopstick. "I kinda thought I could put it together in a lot less time than it took. But you know, things sort of got involved, things didn't quite fit the same on the site. There were crossbars on it [the steel frame] when it was being jostled around and being worked

GHOSTLY
The dream clock is gone and the stairwell is just an empty place. Get the stairs …

SPENCE'S DELIVERY SERVICE
Mike Spence hustles the main service door panel to the site.

on, and when it was brought [to the workshop] from Tech it had these cross-members, which kept it all straight. When we bolted it down, it went out of skew a little bit, and all those holes we'd carefully put in, there wasn't much tolerance in those holes."

In the workshop, they had aligned all the side panels successfully. Then Saunders removed the panels and sent them off for sandblasting and antiquing. This made the job of fitting the inner workings easier; he could reach all the bolts and screws with no trouble. Now, on the street, with the frame skewed, to reach where he needed to reach to place things, let alone screw them tight, was not so straightforward, even when the holes occasionally lined up.

"We just never thought of undoing the bolts to see. We just sort of shimmed it and got it plumb, up and down, but it can be up and down straight and still be skewed a bit. We had an awful time getting all the bronze sides on—it was stressful that way. Everything that could go wrong went wrong."

By enlarging some holes and using a pry bar, they got three side panels snugged up to the frame. That was hard enough, but fitting the corner mouldings, which had some fairly close tolerances, was tougher, creating more delay and suspense. And there were the inside parts still to install. This was harder than city council politics.

Hey, Look—A Crane!

By the time the top cube (the square unit that holds the clock works and clock faces, and supports the roof and gutters and steam whistles—the user interface in today's parlance) rose up the elevator shaft, across the dock, down the alley, and around to the site, it was late Thursday night. There were no sidewalk superintendents to irritate or reporters to spill the beans, Saunders remembered, "but it wasn't easy tripping over your own feet in the dark."

A Vancouver Engineering truck with a "cherry picker" crane showed up, just when it was needed, to hoist the top cube up and over. With the plastic roof pulled aside, the top cube was gently lowered through the roof opening onto the frame. Who organized the cherry picker? Strangely enough, Saunders doesn't know.

Jon Ellis didn't arrange it. He had nothing to do with the clock installation. He thinks the city probably didn't provide it officially. If someone in the engineering department orchestrated it, there would have been extensive administrivia: approval processes to go through, double-time pay for the operator, and related time-wasters.

Ellis suspects some city worker or other had a cherry picker in the neighbourhood and may have just jumped into the fray unofficially,

WAITING FOR A LIFT

Johnny Podlesnick and Saunders pose while waiting for the cherry picker.

THE TOP CUBE DESCENDS

The plastic bag of wiring is directed inside the frame as the top cube swings down.

since many of the people involved with the re-creation of Gastown would "hang" there after work and socialize. It was the centre of their world in those days and they were eager to help out.

Saunders's other artist/employee, George Webster, helped move the parts to the site and was up all Friday night with Saunders and Spence. Spence remembers that Webster was dating the sister of one of the city workers on the crane truck that night. Maybe love does make the world go round.

It's all speculation, however, and the question remains one of many minor mysteries that pop up throughout the steam clock's eventful history.

MIDNIGHT OIL

The only lighting they had was a tiny clip-on light that wasn't bright enough to dispel the dark shadows. So they switched places frequently to find and tighten the fasteners, alternating one set of tired eyes with the other to relieve the strain. With hindsight, Saunders says, "Taking even one of the side panels off again would have made all the difference, but we were too tired and too stressed to think clearly."

With the top cube fastened, Saunders and Spence, with one of them squeezed inside and the other hanging on the outside, bolted the top cove piece over the motion works and attached the gutters.

A CIRCUS PERFORMANCE
Rubberman bends around corners to attach the top cube to the frame top.

SAUNDERS CATCHES SOME Z'S
... while waiting for steam feed-pipes to be installed.

TOGETHERNESS
Saunders does his monkey imitation with a wrench to attach pieces.

Periodically, Saunders paused to dangle himself from the hoarding with one hand while taking pictures of their progress with the other. Eventually, a weary Saunders lifted the roof by hand and fastened it in place. Finally, five gleaming brass steam whistles were attached.

By now, exhaustion was beginning to take its toll. And the beer made them all drowsy. Eyelids drooped, wrenches slipped, and knuckles were skinned. Motion slowed while time seemed to accelerate. Decisions became hard to make. At about two in the morning, their bodies surrendered and dragged their brains home to grab a few hours of sleep.

From Trials to Tribulations

A HOT SHOWER
The towel on Saunders's head was to soak up hot water dripping from condensation on the plastic ceiling.

Early Friday morning, Saunders was back on the job, exhausted and feeling grungy (hung over?). Perhaps when Gassy Jack started Gastown, he served up the whiskey to his bar-building volunteers as a reward after the work was done. "Working in the wet and the heat inside the hoarding maybe had something to do with that," claimed Saunders. From then on, fruit juice, water, and energy snacks consumed Saunders's beer budget.

The steam clock case and major parts were installed. Now all they needed was another week to assemble the inside workings, test them, close up and veil the clock, and remove the hoarding in preparation for the unveiling ceremony. Four days in a pinch. They had twenty-eight hours.

With cool air outside and condensed steam inside and the water staying in and time running out, Saunders and his crew started to install and connect parts together. The term "tight spot" was getting a new definition. Forgoing sleep, they raced toward the deadline hour. In a non-stop blitz, it was done. Slick as a steam whistle—except ...

Time and effort had been saved by only partially pre-assembling the clock. Not clearly envisioned at the time were the consequences for shortcutting the job that way: how so many of the ends left loose (or completely untied) would come back at them via the proverbial fan.

It Rained Inside

Who would have thought it? More rain—inside now!

Once everything was inside the hoarding, a person could be forgiven for thinking the worst was over. That person would be wrong. Remember, the prime purpose of the steam clock was to conceal the vents of an underground steam distribution system. Those vents were now, necessarily, inside what amounted to a sealed construction shed. It was nice and warm inside, if rather moist. Good, thought the assembly crew.

But it was nearer the end of September than the beginning, and cool outside compared to the steamy temperature inside. The laws of physics took over. Moisture condensed so rapidly under the plastic sheet roof that it actually rained inside. The box of fasteners was wrapped in plastic to keep dry. Once opened, it filled, and the plastic wrapping served only to keep the water in. Saunders and Spence soon gave up on dry parts, simply upending and draining the box whenever they needed fasteners.

The inside rain was nice and warm, at least, but steam venting from the control room below had nowhere to go. "The steam vapour was in your face, making it almost impossible to work," recalls Spence with Saunders's quick agreement. In desperation, they stuffed rags into the vent holes and then covered them with scrap boards. "Not so good for the control room, but a whole lot better for us," says Saunders, as they worked around the clock on the clock to complete its installation.

Spence, artist, employee, and steam clock installer sans pareil, was at Saunders's elbow from start to finish. Spence claims through all the stress and tension—the delays, screw-ups, and a seemingly endless parade of frustrations—that "Ray never lost his cool." Says Spence, "You knew he was upset when he got a little red in the forehead. It was from the discipline of working with clocks and watches; you can't lose your cool with them or you just wreck your work."

Frenzy

The ladder was too small, the hoarding too tight, and boxes of parts were squished in. The steam pipe insulation took up room they had not expected. There was no clearance for tools and no room for hands to turn. The floodlights installed above were helpful but created shadows. It was hard to fit and hold parts and line up holes to fasten them in places you couldn't see. Saunders even gave himself a shock, so he turned off the breaker inside the clock. The steam fogged up their specs. Every part and every tool was as slick as a wet whistle from the hot rain. They reworked, bent, pried, hammered, twisted, and prayed in the struggle to get the clock together in time.

As unveiling day approached, like a cloud with a tarnished lining, even the steam engine was unwilling to meet the deadline. Saunders had included an electric motor as backup to the engine—for when it

SAUNDERS KEPT WORKING

The pre-drilled holes didn't want to align: every screw and bolt was another challenge.

WIRES TO GO

The wires are for lighting and the steam solenoid valves that control the whistles.

needed service. The backup motor was put in gear. You can imagine Burt's head nodding approval.

In a few hours, the city would celebrate! There would be a parade. There would be free concerts. There would be food and there would be drink. The Gastown Business Improvement Society was sponsoring a community promotional event, and the clock's unveiling ceremony would be a key part of the weekend-long celebration. A large stage was already assembled, local politicians and celebrities were lined up, radio and television crews were on their way; the event was being trumpeted far and wide. The Gastown Steam Clock's unveiling would be a local event of note.

With every minute, time tightened around them! At about four in the morning on Saturday, Spence and Webster crashed in the shop for a couple of hours' sleep. Saunders kept working.

THE DEADLINE IS SET

Saunders better be ready, Burt's method and all. His time-outs are all used up.

THE WARM-UP ACT

An unidentified street performer juggles for the crowd and his supper.

THE NATIVES ARE RESTLESS

It's an eager crowd waiting to see the world's first steam clock come on line.

THE LAST MINUTES

There was no turning back; the deadline (and public humiliation) loomed. The band was playing, the Gastown Fall Festival Parade was streaming past the hoarding, and the main access door was still sitting on the ground awaiting installation. Beside the access door, a cloth veil waited to be draped over the sixteen-foot-high steam clock; and the wooden hoarding still had to come down.

But ready or not, unveiling was in an hour—the sign said so. "The politicians will stall the crowd. Thank God for politicians!" (What a dizzying thought.) At 11:00 a.m., Saunders and Spence lifted the access door into place with great grunting and gnashing of teeth. By this time, it came as no surprise that the hinge pins refused to line up with the waiting pin holes. It had fit in the workshop, but now, with the music mounting, a crowd accumulating, and politicians posturing, it didn't.

The hinges "weren't even close," says Saunders. A glass and brass beauty, roughly two feet by four feet and weighing over a hundred pounds, the door didn't care about deadlines or unruly crowds. Desperate, Saunders and Spence finally gave up on their attempted surgery and just jammed it into place, whacking it with a two-by-four to make sure it was wedged tight. Precision engineering takes many forms.

Throwing their tools into the shopping buggy, Saunders thought, I'll put the hinge pins in tomorrow. By leaving a few non-essentials for later, like condensation drain pipes, time tuning, and the door hinges, they made the deadline—sort of.

The Blubbering Horologist

When Saunders opened the hoarding to hobble off and change into his ceremonial finery, there were his three children from his first marriage: Jim, Marion, and Julia. They had come with their mother to see the unveiling of their daddy's obsession. Marion, apparently an observant nine-year-old, gave him quite a surprise. After casting a critical eye on Saunders's creation, she piped up with no hint of doubt, "Dad, you did a good job."

Saunders lost it; tears welled up. This was the culmination of three years of struggle and uncertainty and hard work; like the recalcitrant door, he came completely unhinged. Worse, he could not pull it together—he was just "sobbing and wailing."

Wiping his leaky eyes, Saunders, taking the tool buggy with him, headed off to change steam-clock-building clothes into steam-clock-unveiling clothes. He could not practise his speech at all because he was crying buckets. With all the rushing and all that blubbering, might a few things have been missed? Testing the ad hoc mechanisms, for example, or flicking a switch?

SAUNDERS BLUBBERS

And what father wouldn't blubber after a daughter praises his work?

VEIL ON—VEIL OFF

As Saunders headed off to change his clothes, Spence unboxed the donation from Roy and Dorothy Pegler. There's not supposed to be any lettering on it, he thought. With the hoarding still to be taken down and carted away, there was nothing for it but to drape the black, custom-made, sixteen-foot-long veil over the star attraction, mysterious lettering and all. Spence hooked it up to the wire frame and quick-release mechanism he had made and attached a long pull-rope. And a tidy little untested Burt's method assembly it was. With the veil now on, the hoarding could come down.

While speakers assembled on the dignitaries' stage that had been set up in the street, the crew, which now included several police officers ostensibly on site for crowd control, hammered and crow-barred away at the hoarding. And so, in not much more than fifteen minutes, the steam clock stood, enshrouded in black—except for the advertisement that covered it from roof gutters to sidewalk.

The fundraising committee, begging and borrowing, had raised thousands of dollars in donations. In return, they had offered each donor only a very small spot on a bronze plaque, along with every other donor, as an advertising opportunity. And here the black veil was, sporting a huge pitch for Roy and Dorothy's lingerie business. In Saunders's words, it was "an ostentatious advertisement."

Yes, the Pegler's gift horse was revealed to be a costume, our generous panty makers holding up the head while all the other Gastown merchants were left wearing the horse's posterior! It caused more than a minor dust-up and a loud outcry of righteous, and in some cases undoubtedly envious, wrath. Recriminations flew in all directions, but mostly at the head of the gift horse. But the deed was done; and don't you harbour a grudging respect for such an impudent improvisation?

HIGH NOON—THE REVEAL

The platform was crowded. Amongst many others there were Mayor Jack Volrich who, in keeping with the spirit of the occasion, was a little behind schedule; former mayor Art Phillips, who voted for and donated to the clock fund; Councillor May Brown, Gastown's "rep" on council; the otherwise unemployed Ace Asen, for many years colourful Lord Mayor of Gastown (unofficial); Emery Barnes, football player turned politician; and others including, eventually, Ray Saunders and his moist eyes. It was a large stage.

EAGER HELPERS

One of Vancouver's finest, caught up in the moment, pitches in to remove the hoarding along with (from left to right) Mr. Spence, Randy Smith, Mike Spence, John Podlesnick, and the soon-to-be-infamous Roy Pegler.

A SURPRISE GIFT HORSE

The hoarding goes—and the Pegler's advertorial artistry is revealed.

ALMOST READY

Spence installs his custom-designed unveil rigging.

MURPHY'S FIRST STRIKE

Something in Spence's rigging was built too well to give when tugged, and the veil hangs.

OH OH!

Ellis, Saunders (centre with Mayor Volrich), and other dignitaries admire Murphy's work.

After an hour or so of speeches, mutual backslapping, and no shortage of puffery about the success of the Gastown redevelopment project, the crowd got restless. Enough with the words, it was time. With great fanfare, a dollop of enthusiasm, and a soupçon of innocence, Art Phillips pulled the rope.

Now, Spence's veil-quick-release-gadget was simple: two wires laid across the gutters. They were both attached to a rope that led to the podium on the stage. Former mayor Phillips pulled one of the wires out cleanly but the other caught, leaving the veil dangling.

It hung there, like a hospital gown, not revealing but not concealing either, rather accentuating the lumps and bumps. Phillips huffed and puffed and to shouts of "pull it again" gave a second, stronger tug and the veil completed its interrupted descent.

What a relief. Mayor Jack Volrich stepped up to announce the official inauguration of the new Gastown landmark—the innovative and amazing Gastown Steam Clock—then pushed the button to start the clock whistles. Nothing.

TA DA!

And there it is, all dolled up and far prettier than a cement planter.

Problem?

It was classic. More than a thousand people had assembled to experience the start of the world's first steam clock … or for the free hot dogs. Officials could be seen through a layer of egg; dignitaries were pretending that nothing was wrong; and the crowd, straining to hear "The Westminster Chimes," caught only the sound of their own breathing.

Then there was Saunders, administering a mental slap to his forehead, remembering he had turned the power breaker off during installation when he was shocked by crowding wires. I forgot to turn the power back on!

Although an artist, Saunders was not a complete stranger to sequential logic: I have to get the small service door open again and turn the breaker back on—and fast! Saunders leapt from the podium and reached into his pocket—to no avail. He was dressed up! There are zero tools in my pockets, he realized! Where is the Allen key? The steam clock service door was locked by an Allen key, and any knowledge of its current location was no longer resident in Saunders's mind—nor could Spence help! They were both brain dead by this time, having had less than one night's sleep between them in the previous two days.

The hand tools and other loose bits had found their way into the tool buggy in a disorganized clangour in the last minute tizzy of tidying, and then been parked down the back lane halfway to Saunders's shop. Hoping against hope, Saunders, in a frantic scramble for the elusive key, dove deep into the buggy.

No Problem!

And who doesn't enjoy watching a politician stabbing desperately at a lifeless start button? And what politician doesn't relish the opportunity to extemporize an extra half hour to a restless crowd waiting to hear a clock toot its tune after three years of steamy promises? Whatever they said, they earned their keep that day, covering the moment of silence where a loud hoot was expected—and the ensuing wait while Saunders fixed the problem.

And the Allen key was there, at the very bottom of course. Saunders, rushing it to the clock, opened the cover and flipped the power switch. Soon, the whistles played their brassy tune and the big whistle blasted even the memory of that sound-of-silence into a distant future. Saunders had his moment of glory, although his emotions were still wobbly from his daughter's innocent praise. In the end, he just had to ignore himself, get up and blubber a speech into a fistful of microphones and no fewer than five TV cameras. Of course, he can't remember a single word of it!

So finally, on September 24, 1977, the Gastown Steam Clock was unveiled. They were a little late to the party—two years and thirty minutes late—but it was a great party, with bands and costumes and hot dogs. Gastown finally had its unique steam clock, at least for a few days.

PARTY TIME
Saunders and helper Randy Smith schmooze, cups overflowing with a sense of victory—well earned.

CREATIVE METAL TEAM
Spence was an artist working on contract with Saunders. He pitched in to help grind the rough bronze case sections painstakingly to a smooth, lustrous finish and was Saunders's right-hand man during the installation phase. Margie Meinzinger and Susie Schultz helped to keep the studio going, handling clerical, sales, and apprentice sculpting duties, as did Sue (2) (Saunders and Spence have gone blank on her last name).

George Webster, also a metal sculptor and steam clock volunteer, worked through most of the night of September 23, 1977, helping to install the clock. Randy Smith, artist trainee, famous for the ethereal beauty of his many girlfriends, helped with the construction hoarding and clock parts transportation between workshop and assembly site. Saunders was underfoot for all of it.

A MOTIVATED TEAM
Everyone got into a picture for posterity: L to R, Mike Spence, Margie Meinzinger, Susie Schultz, Sue (?), George Webster, Randy Smith, and Raymond Saunders.

~~Ray~~

JULY 10   13h30

COMPLAINT whistles always on (sometime earlier)
                                    today
ONLY PART OF NOTES (SAY 10 of 12 or JUST THE
   PLAYED   BIG "BLAST")

OBSERVED:

LOOSE

LEVER
OUT OF
GUIDE

MERCURY
SWITCH

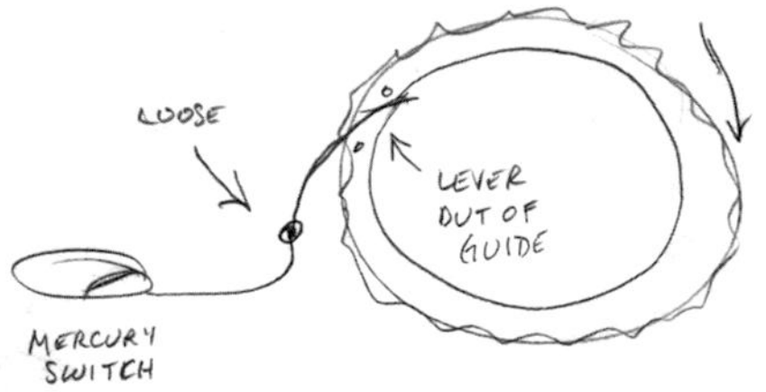

← POOR
  "ROCKER"
  ACTION.
- NOT ENOUGH
  TRAVEL
  EVERY TIME

PROBLEMS WITH
TUNE MACHINE

I SHUT OFF "WHISTLES" CIRCUIT BREAKER, POSTED
                                      NOTICE.

Regards —
Mike

LIFE ON
THE STREET

A TEAM EFFORT

Individuals, families, tourists, newlyweds and lovers, protesters and activists, even visiting sports teams—all come to Gastown to have their picture taken with the steam clock. Often, all at the same time!

LIFE ON THE STREET

The Gastown Steam Clock was no longer just a dream; it was a real, mostly working, steam clock. It's the mostly that brought Saunders out with Mike Spence, away from their well-earned Sunday morning sleep-in. With visions of crushed pedestrians dancing in their heads, who could sleep? Besides, it was fun to be out there! The pressure was off—at least the pressure to get it done—and the relief put a spring in everyone's step.

So what if the door was being ornery? The problem looked a lot more manageable now, and they pushed and pressed and pounded and pried with renewed energy. But again, nothing! Not until they created some flexibility by loosening all of the frame brackets could they finally mount the door onto its hinges.

On Monday Johnny Podlesnick and Ralph Johnstone of Central Heat worked from morning to night to install drain pipes from the steam manifold. Two of the steam whistles were out of tune and the big whistle was a bit loud. But it was together and working—bringing the long-delayed steam clock project to a successful conclusion. Except for getting the steam engine working and the whistles tuned and ...

In August, a month or so before the clock was scheduled for installation, Saunders had fulfilled another promise: he took a day off from clockmaking to marry Dr. Laurie Kanke. What does a wife do when a steam clock project delays her honeymoon? She waits! Her husband's passion, after all, had been pre-empted by a steam clock that had consumed every cent and every minute Saunders could spare for the past three years. Now the newlyweds could pack for a belated Hawaiian honeymoon.

It worked for a few days. Then it didn't. The clock, probably broken-hearted at being left behind, broke down. The balls were not falling right—the clock was screwed up. Saunders, showing a belated grasp of appropriate priorities, put up a sign—On Honeymoon. Back in ten days—and flew off to Hawaii. And the clock sat, wearing its crooked sign in lonely misery.

Which rather set the stage for the next thirty years of what some might call a dysfunctional relationship between Saunders, the clock, the city, and an unexpected invasion of tourists.

FITTING PIPES

Johnny Podlesnick and Ralph Johnstone of Central Heat install drains.

THE PLAQUES GO ON

Johnstone and Podlesnik of Central Heat replace the plaque after installing drain pipes the Monday after the unveiling.

VICISSITUDES

WOW!

Saunders can't believe his steam clock is actually finished.

All too soon, or not soon enough, the honeymoon was over. There ensued a desperate scramble to tinker the drive and lift chains back into motion and get the steam engine working. Saunders reworked the moving parts, some to fit better and others to last longer. Steam engine modifications were completed and from July 1978 it chugged happily away ... until the first ninety days were up and the warranty expired.

That's in jest, but clock maintenance did challenge Saunders again, and challenges the city engineers responsible for the clock to the present day. However, not all the ensuing complications were internal to the clockworks. The first, a very serious problem indeed, came from an unexpected direction.

HhOOOOOO…! "My ears! Could somebody shut that thing off? I can't even hear my sewing machine."

It was Monday, September 26, 1977, and the steam clock was two days old. While having the world's first steam clock would prove to be a lot of fun, it would also be a lot like having a baby: pride and amusement in precarious balance with plenty of maintenance demands augmented by the occasional screaming tantrum.

A SHORT HISTORY

Too short—it skips over the good stuff: Gassy Jack and William Cornelius Van Horne and the big fire and Rudyard Kipling and a host of other people and events.

TOO MUCH STEAM

A reduction valve reduced the steam pressure from 235 pounds per square inch (psi) in the main pipe to 75 psi for the clock. It made a lovely sound, but deafeningly loud to anyone standing within a city block when the clock whistled every hour. The city had specified a two-block maximum range, but at 75 psi the decibel level went way beyond the limit. Jon Ellis said, "You could hear it in Nanaimo" (on Vancouver Island some forty miles away, so perhaps he exaggerated). The racket was so great it was startling and is known to have frightened children into tears. The crowning blow to the high pressure tune came when the ladies threatened to stop sewing. It happened like this ...

Townline Sportswear inhabited the second floor of the Leckie Building, above Roy and Dorothy Pegler's panty factory and kitty-corner to our steam clock. The sportswear seamstresses found the clock whistles so loud and intrusive that they quickly decided to go out on strike if something was not done.

Townline complained to city hall and invited city representatives, Gastown Merchants Association representatives, and Saunders to a meeting in their second-floor boardroom. The boardroom windows looked over the steam clock from across the street, directly in line with the steam whistles. The meeting was scheduled for precisely twelve noon and the owner of Townline Sportswear, no fool he, had the windows open. Just as they started the meeting, the clock instructed its four tune whistles and the grand finale boat whistle to sound off—and virtually blew the meeting into the street!

Saunders recalls, "The sound was actually painful. I had to cover my ears!"

A TIGHT FIT

Getting in and out of the Water Street control room is accomplished through a manhole, the cover of which is right beside the steam clock. You could be standing right over a technician while you are looking into the clock.

AN EASY FIX

Of course the ladies' point was made on the instant, loud and clear. As soon as the whistles stopped blowing, the question was put, "How can we work in this atmosphere?" Saunders acknowledged, "There's no need for any more discussion," and they humbly rose and went to arrange a solution.

Re-engineering the whistles to blow quietly would have cost a bundle, and as usual there was no bundle to be had. A call went out to Central Heat, and the next day a steam technician removed the manhole cover and descended to the steam room under the clock. He gave a half-turn or two to the pressure-reducing valve, turning the pressure down from 75 to 17 psi, which was as low as it could go

PEOPLE BELOW

An exhaust vent is built into the ceiling of the control room, exiting through the base of the steam clock. Cool air comes in through a second vent on the other side of the clock base.

The resulting convection current keeps the room cool enough to allow maintenance technicians to check and repair insulation, pipes, gauges, solenoids, and valves without cooking themselves.

and still produce a sound from the big whistle. Et voilà, no more screech!

The resulting basso profundo, tone-deaf breathiness of the whistled tune was unexpected and disconcerting. It made the clock sound like a drunken sailor with asthma. Would a tone-deaf clock prove to be more acceptable than the more tunefully exuberant one? Was this to be the end of the steam clock? Would cement tree-planters make a comeback? Were the dreams of Jon Ellis and Ray Saunders and everyone who worked and fought and donated to have a unique architectural artifact in Gastown about to go up in steam?

Amazingly, few seemed troubled enough by the dissonance to complain and the steam clock's popularity never flagged. Even so, the whistles were re-machined in 1979 to work better with the lowered steam pressure. It wasn't enough to make the tune tuneful. Saunders was asked by one honest and forthright Japanese tourist, "How often does it make the noise?" Still, the clock, the steam, and the semi-musical sounds of both the whistles and Saunders's puffery (on his frequent visits) never failed to entertain and amuse their audience.

A Fine Funding Finish

Saunders and the Steam Clock Fundraising Committee were left deep in the red, with no apparent way out. Nonetheless, the clock was meeting its obligations and fortunately made a good impression in the right quarters. A public-spirited philanthropist anonymously donated more than $20,000 so that the fundraising committee, and Saunders, could pay off their steam clock debts.

Out of debt at last, the steam clock could relax and enjoy its growing popularity midst a trouble-free existence. Musicians and panhandlers took up their stations below the clock, some athletic individual went for a stroll on the roof, and one man, apparently upset by the presence of electricity in the workings, beat it with a hammer. And over time, the steam clock periodically played host to other signs of social unrest.

Is It a Revolution?

On a night in the 1990s, a party of persons was crowded around the steam clock, waiting for the midnight whistle. Now, this was a rowdy bunch: talking and laughing, singing and shouting, whooping and hollering—and generally having a raucous time of it.

So much so, in fact, that the local constabulary felt it appropriate to stop and see what was up, i.e., calm the crowd and, if necessary,

ANONYMOUS THANK YOU

How do you say thanks to a contributor who wants to remain anonymous? One way was to give top billing to "Anonymous Donor" on the Donors Plaque when it was installed (years later).

But anybody can do that. Saunders could do something else. Melting down some leftover bronze cuttings from the clock case, he sculpted the generous benefactor a one-of-a-kind bronze model of the steam clock, set on a base of moss jade retrieved from the Fraser River near Hope, B.C.

arrest the ringleaders for being drunk and disorderly. A quite likely action as the partiers were variously bollixed, barley basted, blitzed, or embalmed—in other words, anything but sober.

After some fast talking, undoubtedly laced with calorific carbohydrates offered for the officers' egos, the red-eyed revellers were left to their own devices by the undoubtedly envious emissaries of public order, but only upon their sober promise to be good, or at least to be careful.

Fat chance! Did I mention it was New Year's Eve?

Yes indeed, New Year's Eve, the excuse for any number of perilous pranks performed by potted poltroons. On this occasion, it was deemed sufficient reason for miscellaneous fireworks to be shot off, with drunken deliberation, in all directions.

The red-eyed revellers eventually found aiming a Roman candle beyond their reduced capacities and were saved from shooting a bystander only by the good graces of whichever saint had pulled the duty for that year. (Is there a Patron Saint of Drunken Fools?)

If this sort of thing kept up, the clock's reputation could suffer. But there was good news too.

GASTOWN TO WHISTLER RACE

Started as a Gastown promotional event, a race between Vancouver's city planners and engineers, Jon Ellis confesses that the first bicycle race was rigged! Apparently, certain committed planners needed engineering support in their efforts to make Gastown successful as a commercial and tourist destination. The trophy was engraved with the winner's name (the engineers) before the race was run.

THE TOUR DE GASTOWN

For many years an honest competition, last run in 2008. Check the web site for updates and see www.tourdegastown.com/rd_photos.htm# for a photo history. B.C.'s "big" bicycle races now include BMX, cross country, and trail races, including the B.C. Bike Race, a seven-day mountain-bike stage race from Vancouver to Whistler, by way of Vancouver Island.

Fame ...

> It's the best clock in the world for those who don't care what time it is.
>
> – Jon Ellis

"The steam clock is successful because it wasn't built by committee," says Ellis. "It couldn't happen today; the civic bureaucracy has grown so many committees and rules to control public art in public places that it has become a roadblock to creativity."

Pioneering Spirit

"Gastown was a fun place to be in the seventies," says Ellis, originator and champion of the steam clock idea. A report from a Quebec lawyer to the United Nations emphasized the importance of a pioneering community spirit in the successful redevelopment of Gastown—and by extrapolation the Gastown Steam Clock.

Out of that creative stew came a rejuvenated and lively downtown core and an incredible cascade of innovations and initiatives that wove into the social fabric of not only Vancouver, but also British Columbia and all of Canada. Heading the list were legalized Sunday shopping, gambling fundraisers for non-profit associations, provincial sanction for local business improvement associations, cultural creations such as the Gastown Grand Prix (later the Tour de Gastown) and the Vancouver International Jazz Festival, and many artistic endeavours like the steam clock and the Gassy Jack statue.

Ellis is nothing short of humble about his role in the Gastown renewal and the creation of the steam clock, describing events as if he were simply an observer. Yet rooting through extensive files and memorabilia, old newspapers, magazines, books, and miscellaneous bits and pieces, there is one name that keeps popping up, and that is Jon Ellis.

He most assuredly did not do all the work, but perhaps the word "catalyst" would apply when describing his roles. He developed the idea in the face of loud objections, found someone to build it despite many rejections, and gained support to raise funds and overcome budget restrictions. And he won official approval for the project in spite of bureaucratic resistance. All this was a trifling side-issue to his main job as a Gastown planner and project manager.

"[I am] surprised how it survived, that it actually works, that people don't seem to care if it keeps the time, and by the degree of success it has achieved. We had no idea that would happen."

1977–A HAPPENING YEAR IN VANCOUVER

The steam clock shares its birth year with, amongst other happenings, establishment of the Wreck Beach Preservation Society, the appointment of B.C.'s first native woman judge, and the opening of the Vancouver Harbour Centre (at the time the tallest building in Vancouver at 461 feet).

The SeaBus ferry service started, the Italian Cultural Centre opened, Willy de Roos sailed through the Northwest Passage to Vancouver in SV *Williwaw*, Jack Volrich succeeded Art Phillips as mayor, and the Orpheum Theatre became the new home of the Vancouver Symphony Orchestra. *Star Wars* premiered, and three movies were made in Vancouver, notably *Greenpeace–Voyages to Save the Whales*.

Vancouver's first World's Worst Art Auction was held for the British Columbia Paraplegic Foundation, British Columbia Women's Hospital and Health Centre delivered baby number 100,000, and construction of Children's Hospital began.

For more information on these and many other events, check out the innovative web site project of the late Chuck Davis at www.vancouverhistory.ca or visit the Vancouver Public Library's heritage section.

THE GOOD POINTS

With hindsight, it doesn't seem so surprising: the steam clock has a lot going for it. Its success starts with a great setting, the renovated Gastown, drawing people to the area and acting as the perfect backdrop to the steam clock. The clock looks like it has been there for a hundred years. And it has serious artistic merit. Who knew a steam clock could be so beautiful? Maybe it's one of those form-following-function things, making it not only pleasing to the eye, but also satisfying to the soul—just a guess.

It's unique as well, being the world's first, and for a time only, public steam clock. It also counts usefulness amongst its virtues: safely and attractively venting Central Heat's underground steam equipment control room (its original raison d'être), telling the time (not well, but well enough), serving as a landmark for friends and lovers to find one another, and being a tourist attraction of note—all in all doing more for the success of Gastown than quite possibly any other single factor.

And what a great toy! Most of humanity is fascinated by gadgetry, and if the steam clock is anything, it's a great gadget. The fascination of watching it toot out "The Westminster Chimes" is enjoyed by visitors from all over the globe. Kids love it. Engineers are intrigued by it. Horologists are enthusiastic about it. Architects and town planners admire and respect it. And you and I are entertained by it.

Everything people build should be half so successful.

THE GHOST OF GASTOWN

Mary Drew wrote a wonderfully whimsical book for children, *Gastown Stories*, which included an imaginative tale entitled "The Ghost of Gastown." Appearing in the steam, especially thick in the cooler winter months, gathering around the clock, the ghost swirls around so quickly the clock is splattered with mud and can't concentrate on keeping time.

The book, illustrated by animator Norman Drew, stars little heroine Chika, from his animated film series *Chika's Magic Sketch Book*. Courageous Chika traps the ghost in her shawl, and of course cleans the clock.

Vancouver Public Library possesses a number of copies in its Canadiana section.

A FAMILY AFFAIR

Look at the steam make music … fascinating.

LIGHTING UP THE NIGHT

Creating a welcoming beacon in the darkness

THE DREW CREW

The illustrator, a young actress hired to portray the heroine, and the author of the tale "The Ghost of Gastown"

A TOUR BUS DESTINATION

Tour buses flocked to Gastown after the steam clock was installed.

A HAPPENIN' PLACE

The steam clock becomes a focal point for street activities and entertainment.

WE CAN FIX THIS!

Children trust the steam clock—it helps to build their self-e-steam.

It Started Off Well

"Where does the steam come from?" became an oft-heard question under the clock, when the whistles stopped blowing their tune. Saunders began a questionable tradition when his response developed into a stock answer, "from boiling water." Only when the groaning lets up does he break down and tell how the local private utility, Central Heat Distribution Limited, siphons off a bit of the hot stuff from their underground steam distribution pipe for the steam clock to use.

Across the street, George Taramarcaz had named his restaurant the Brasserie de L'Horloge in a fit of optimism back in 1975, when the steam clock was originally promised. Now that the clock was in place at last, he no longer had to launch into a convoluted explanation to answer his patrons' innocent questions: "Why the name L'Horloge?" and "What clock?"

Then a tour guide operator started flying Japanese tourists in with the promise of, amongst Vancouver's other attractions, a steam clock to photograph. Soon, the streets were inundated by tourists from all

FASCINATING ...

Ya know, I bet I could make one of these.

NOT JUST FOR KIDS

People of all ages get their picture taken with the steam clock for their memories—including Saunders's parents Marion and Milton Saunders.

nations, by local gawkers, and by eager photo essayists. Tour buses began to block the short side street and crowd the sidewalks.

The words "steam clock" spread like soft butter. People came to see the Gastown marvel and hear it toot. Initially, they came in dribs and drabs. Soon, the neighbours started to drop by to check it out. From the United States, from the Upper Fraser Valley, and finally from around the block and down the street, they came to see what the fuss was about.

THE LEGEND GROWS

Gastown became a world-renowned urban redevelopment success, and while commercial viability of the rejuvenated Gastown received mixed reviews, few cared about the Gastown Steam Clock's imperfections—it was and remains an unalloyed success. It has been telling time, blowing whistles, and entertaining admirers for thirty-three years and counting at this writing. The design and setting are so effective that many people are surprised to discover it has been around for only a third of a century and not the hundred and more years its appearance would suggest.

A surprise to its builders as well, the steam clock experienced success greater than all expectations. In fact, it became an international star. It's a safe bet that the clock has been viewed, admired, and examined by many millions in its short life.

Loved also by artists, photographers, and writers, it has been sketched, painted, sculpted, copied, emulated, and photographed. Estimates of the number of photographs taken over the years boggle the mind—it may well be in the billions. And it's a popular subject for crafty bookmarks, business card holders, name and address books, postcards and greeting cards, etchings, paintings, statues, models, T-shirts, and more, not to mention interviews, articles, and even advertisements.

POSITIVE REVIEWS

Monetary gains ensued as the clock titillated curious travellers. Tourism profits and rents grew, as did the city's tax revenues.

JAMMING WITH THE BOYS

The steam clock is popular with street musicians too—good vibes!

A GREAT SPOT

It's fun to be at the centre of Gastown's many parades and events.

Not just a tourist destination, the clock became a local landmark and a rendezvous point for young and old. "I think it's great. I see it at least ten times every year. I like the steam that shoots out to tell the time," said a local teen. He added, "It's not working like it should. I think they should fix it. It's one of the best attractions they have. My friends, they just stop by, check out the clock once it goes off. They all like to hang out around there."

A feeling of ownership and accomplishment seems to come along with showing the steam clock to guests from around the world. One occasional visitor said, "I think we all like gadgetry, especially when it's not electronic. It's something unique. I think it is part of Gastown. [If it were gone] I'd feel a sense of loss."

A young teenager said, "It seems interesting; the noise and steam made me want to learn more about it."

Says another youth, "My friends and I always go to the steam clock and listen to it go off a few times."

It's part of their Gastown ritual!

Even newlyweds have travelled to Gastown just to have their wedding pictures taken next to the clock. One young artist, sharing a studio near the clock, also remembers it attracting strange characters, like the handicapped fellow who for many years made a living next to it as a street musician, playing "Somewhere My Love" on a Chinese violin.

THE PRICE OF FAME

As with all stories of stardom, the vicissitudes of daily life took on sometimes heroic proportions.

Sometime between six and nine o'clock on Thursday morning, the first of April 2004, word was leaked to the Canadian Broadcasting Corporation (CBC) that a digital-screen steam clock would soon be replacing the hissing and hooting original. City council was reported to be considering this dastardly deed in the name of safety. The astonished audience of Rick Cluff and *The Early Edition*, CBC Radio One's award-winning morning show, was the first to hear.

Vancouver city councillor Peter Ladner, a guest on the show, supported the idea. He claimed the steam mechanism was outdated and could explode. The plan, Ladner explained, was to replace the existing clock faces with digital screens. These would display, along with the current time, "safe" images of steam and the occasional sponsor's logo.

BUSTED!

A friend of Saunders tells of the time he was sitting in a Gastown restaurant having a beer, cell phone to his ear, explaining to his girlfriend that he wouldn't be able to see her that day as planned as he was detained in Seattle. "You are busted," she said when the steam clock loudly hooted out the hour. "There is no steam clock in Seattle!"

MEASURES OF FAME

A million or more visitors every year, billions of photographs, newspaper and magazine articles, radio and television news reports and practical jokes, children's stories, this book, academic and government studies, etchings, paintings, statues, postcards, bookmarks, coasters, and the ultimate indicator—fridge magnets. You name it, the steam clock continues to be featured in them all.

Saunders, as a local horologist and creator of the steam clock, called in and denounced the proposal, but reminded everyone that the city owned the clock and that he, personally, had no say on this issue of public safety. This only served to incense more of the listeners.

Before the show ended, a barrage of complaints poured into not only the radio station, but also to Peter Ladner's office at City Hall. Said complaints denigrated the plan as both outrageous and egregious. As the angry calls crescendoed, a smug "April Fool" revealed the depths of duplicity being perpetrated on the innocent and very chagrined audience. The fame of Gastown's steam clock was, more or less, official.

VANDALIZED!

The expensive, shatterproof glass kept the inner workings protected from an angry man with a bat.

NEGATIVE VIEWS

Most locals happily accepted the steam clock's popularity. But standing around admiring the clock is one thing; trying to pass by is quite another. Often ambitious photographers, sometimes professionals, but mostly just the curious, intrigued, or amazed spill into the street looking for the perfect composition, incidentally frustrating motorists and enraging couriers, one of whom said, "For a courier, speed is important for making a decent income, so the crowds are very frustrating. I succumbed to temptation on one occasion. As soon as I saw clear road ahead, I put the pedal to the metal. You should have seen them scatter."

A young architect who worked in Gastown for ten years reports that she "walked by the Gastown Steam Clock millions of times—and you can't even get down the sidewalk to have lunch because it's crowded with tourists and they're all circled around the clock and you're trying to elbow your way through and you've looked at the clock but never really seen it and you think, Big deal! Get out of my way! I can't wait for October when the tourists are gone."

I guess it's not for everyone.

BEAUTY IS ITS OWN REWARD

The Gastown Steam Clock is striking, and not just as a pun. Its colours and finish shine—especially to those partial to bronze, copper, and brass. It has artistic merit, being tactile, complex, balanced, and stately. It is also useful, telling the time without being obsessive about precision—as Jon Ellis and others have pointed out—and covering the steam room vent pipes that otherwise would assault pedestrian eyes and kneecaps. A meeting place, reference point, talking point, and fixture, it contributes much to the Gastown ambience. It also entertains jaded senses, stimulates healthy discussion, and provides a marvellous focus for the curious.

With a lifetime of clock collecting and a great horological tradition as a backdrop, it's little wonder that Saunders was imbued with a headful of whimsical notions when first asked if he could build a steam clock. Saunders also continued to annually promote the addition of whimsical clock features and better lighting in his maintenance proposals. But, while the clock attracted tour buses and a great deal of press attention for Vancouver, it was neglected by city budgets. Engineering funds were, in the main, made available for basic maintenance and emergency repairs only.

HAPPY 20TH

Saunders and daughter Julia celebrate with the steam clock on the occasion of its twentieth birthday.

IT'S STUCK ...

George Webster wonders what's wrong—a big problem?

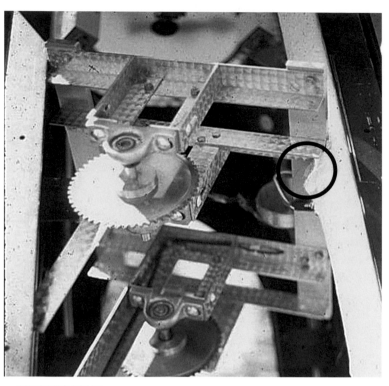

... REALLY STUCK!

What fit just fine in the workshop, now doesn't.

HALFWAY IN, HALFWAY OUT

In the workshop, getting the movement in and out had been simple. Now, out in the open for all to see, the modified support frame gets jammed! It was enough to make Saunders's face red, but was not the first embarrassment, nor the last, he would face in the next thirty-plus years.

Could the door problem they had at the unveiling in '77 have something to do with it? Not likely. What, then? Look at the steam pipe! They'd made allowances in the workshop for the addition of a steam pipe, but they hadn't counted on the insulation being wrapped around it and taking another inch they didn't have to give.

It's time to put good ol' Burt and his "make it work and fix it later" method to work again. Tear off a hunk of insulation, put the clockworks back in, stick the insulation back on the pipe, and it's done.

Later, Saunders added curved brass sheets to cover the inside corners and provide room for the engraved names of all the smaller donors. They gave the clock a more finished look and handily concealed that pesky steam pipe.

KEEPING
THE (COG)
WHEELS
TURNING

STEAM ENGINE PIECES

The steam engine needed frequent service—cleaning corrosion and replacing leaking seals.

Keeping the (Cog) Wheels Turning

Over time, the clock evolved and became quite reliable. But the steam engine did indeed run afoul of steam pressure and friction, and required major maintenance every ninety days or so. The light-duty model kit, even after extensive redesign, was just not tough enough for twenty-four hours a day, seven days a week of operation. Not surprisingly, questions were asked: Isn't maintenance difficult when you mix steam and precision clock workings? Don't things rust up? Do the steam fittings need frequent maintenance?

Steam power and clocks don't go together—just ask any engineer or clockmaker. You would be mistaken if you assumed, just because Saunders ignored the pundits and built a steam-driven clock anyway, that combining steam and time would not produce an obstreperous result. There were many hurdles to overcome in its building, and ever since. The Gastown Steam Clock has indeed faced many challenging mechanical problems in its short life.

STEAM TROUBLE

Saunders at work trying to reduce condensation in the steam manifold. It eventually had to be replaced with a more effective design.

Best Laid Plans

On the advice of city engineers during planning, an extra six inches was added to the height of the base cube to avoid any unseemly encounters between clock and wayward vehicle bumpers. Decorative bollards were also installed to shield pedestrians and the clock from harm. A redesigned steam manifold, in the spring of 1978, arrested a budding steam clock bad habit—spitting! The clock had started spitting hot water on everyone nearby as the whistles played the time. Four new small whistles with their puckers reworked (the tune-playing openings were redesigned to perform better with the lowered pressure) were installed in 1979. Light fixtures for the dials were replaced and a roof-cap air vent added for better humidity control in the top cube.

Then electrical wiring and safety breakers were upgraded. Later improvements included a heated and filtered air intake system, an overhaul for the tune machine, and a motor to replace the variable-speed drill that drove it. In 1995, outside trim was refurbished; and in 1997 the winding chain transmission was replaced.

But, in spite of the sturdy main components and case structure, extraordinary events added to accumulated wear. In 1986, the backup electric motor was promoted to run the lift chain and keep the steam

SPAGHETTI?

The original wiring, all just for the dial lights

HAS TIME STOPPED?

It seems to be working, but the hands aren't going anywhere!

BOLLIXED BOLLARD

Meant to protect the clock, this bollard was driven into it, causing much of the damage.

engine turning. Tune machine challenges eventually led to a computerized tune controller being installed as part of a major overhaul. And the city's engineers made an improved electrical panel that didn't quite fit. New lighting, when installed, left room for further improvement. Robbie Burns would have been proud. Other maintenance work was more noticeable, as ...

When Time Stood Still in Gastown

The steam steamed and the whistles whistled their off-key tune, but the ten minutes past ten just sat there, unchanging, ageless. While not travelling backwards in time, as the clock had when first tested in the workshop, Gastown apparently wasn't travelling forward either!

Calm heads prevailed as Saunders, Gastown's Guru of Horology and Steam Clock Creator, explained. The steam kept steaming and the whistles kept whistling because everything was working—everything but the hands of time. Their gears and drive rods had rusted. An unknown perpetrator—a foolish prankster, irresponsible hoodlum, or perhaps a frustrated mountain climber—had scaled the sixteen-foot-high clock, ascended to the peak, and caused a gutter leak.

A clock doesn't work too well when the moving parts don't move. Hence, Saunders extracted the timekeeping mechanism (the motionworks) and took it to his little shop around the corner for some much needed cleaning and drying. Meanwhile, he replaced the roof and whistles to maintain appearances. It would be ten past ten[1] for another week while he repaired and refurbished the clock's innards.

In what seemed like both forever and no time at all, the gutters and motionworks returned to service—until the next time distortion.

Flood!

Then the lacquer turned white. Sometime in August of 2001, the steam manifold drain plugged and the water backed up. There was no possible reason (went the thinking) for insulating the steam pipe in the bottom of the clock case, so it wasn't. The water level soon rose to a half inch above the steam feed pipe in the base of the clock. Of course it boiled, making it difficult to read the time or see the internal action with steam on the loose and condensation on the windows. In the steam bath, the clock's interior cooked, lending support, one supposes, to the unadventurous viewpoint that "steam and clocks don't mix."

And the rust was back—on everything, this time—and the lacquered parts had cooked in the moist heat. In the end, the whole clock interior had to be stripped and refinished. On a budget, of course, leaving long-standing issues unresolved—again.

A Moving Violation

Saunders felt like he had hardly turned around after fixing the flood and steam damage when, on September 22, 2001, the clock was hit—stricken by a car that just went anywhere its inebriated driver pointed it. By some accounts, the steam clock leaped in front of the wayward automobile to protect nearby pedestrians. A healthy segment of the population (mostly young, but there are believers of all ages) argues that our brave clock heroically sacrificed itself to save those innocents just passing by.

In any event, somehow the foundation moved. The clock tilted, and in the world of mechanical clocks, even the smallest horizontal tendency is a major physical handicap. Adding injury to the insult, a bollard broke off and hit the bottom cube, which cracked.

A cracked cube can be fixed. Getting an out-of-plumb clock back on the up and up, however, is a huge undertaking, possibly requiring the whole clock foundation be dug up and levelled. Saunders resorted once again to Burt's method. He placed temporary shims inside the case and returned just the internal mechanisms to the vertical. Until a major rebuild could be budgeted and scheduled, the clock would just have to be given another name—The Leaning Clock of Gastown?

It's an Ill Wind

… that blows no good—and hopefully something good would come from this unexpected adversity. But at first it looked like an unmitigated disaster. In poor condition before the car accident, the clock now required both major and minor surgery. The neglect leading to this state of affairs included accumulated corrosion (on the outside as well as inside), an overdue tune-machine overhaul, and some long-delayed improvements. With significant accident damage to the clock as well, there was no way to fix it within the annual maintenance budget.

And what if the Insurance Corporation of British Columbia (ICBC), insurer of the guilty car, were to hold the clock fifty per cent responsible for the collision? ICBC often assigns blame for an accident to both parties, the fairness of that assignment occasionally

EASY DOES IT!
The clock is returned to its foundation, without a base cube, which is off for repairs.

NOT SO BAD?
Worse than it looks, it's the bottom cube. And the frame shifted as well—a huge removal and reinstallation repair job.

seeming like a second accident. The clock's reputation for sobriety could be damaged along with its base and bollards!

Estimates were submitted, other repair works coordinated, budgets developed and approved, quotes tendered and verified. The clock's innocence was established and the City of Vancouver and ICBC worked through their tedious decision-making processes to an eventual settlement.

THE LATHE IN ACTION

Saunders polishes a timekeeping cog wheel.

Meanwhile, Gastown's best-known fixture had suffered a steam clock's version of whiplash. It had internal injuries that became progressively more apparent. Saunders tried for months to deduce why the four dials kept going out of sync and what was causing intermittent stoppages that seemed without rhyme or reason. In the end, he removed the roof to find the root of the problems: two connecting-shaft expansion joints out of place and misaligned drive shafts—definitely clock-lash injuries.

Fixing the clock was sometimes dangerous. On one occasion, says Saunders, "I was trying to discover what was wrong with the spring which makes this little loading lever flop back. The lever had moved forward and the spring was very loose and the ball unloaded in a hurry. It went shooting right across and just missed my head. It landed on the street, went bouncing across the street, and a tourist went chasing after it. A fellow from Germany went right out in the street chasing a rolling ball and brought it back." As a token of appreciation, Saunders autographed a steam clock postcard for the accidental assistant.

LIFTING THE LID

More of Burt's method "making it work," trial and error, learn by doing. Eventually they redesigned and replaced the steam manifold.

SHADES OF '77

HhOOOOOO…! "My ears! Could somebody shut that thing off?"

"What's wrong with it?"

It is September 26, 2002, and having the world's first steam clock is still very gratifying, but there are some embarrassing aspects. Twenty-five years old now and it's behaving like a baby again. Vancouverites and regular visitors are accustomed to the traffic snarls and tour buses. But the temper, this non-stop hooting, like a yowling cat. Something has to be done! The call goes out to Ray Saunders from Chris Homewood, the city engineer responsible for the steam clock. "Hi Ray. It's stuck again."

DROPPING BALLS

And once again Saunders drops everything and hurries down to the steam clock, hoping he can get there in time to detect the reason for the problem. This is happening a lot lately and he can't figure out why: a ball keeps falling off, and Saunders has to put it back on the lift chain, adjust the time, and stand there, scratching his head.

"By the time I get there, half the time the machine has reset itself and there's no evidence except the fallen ball. I've stood there for ages on several occasions, but it won't do it while I'm watching. It's as if the darn thing is teasing me. I have to get it fixed—it's just too irritating to ignore."

Saunders eventually found the problem. There is a little guardrail to guide the ball bearings as they roll along the cross-ramp from the top of the lift (up) chain to the top of the drive (down) chain. Slack in the lift chain was leaving a gap between it and the guardrail. Every so often a ball would fall through that gap and jam up the tune machine directly below. The whistle would still blow, but the mechanism that turned the whistle off, couldn't.

BUCKET SEATS

Stainless ball-bearing weights drop from the lift chain into a sloping channel, and then roll down and are pushed into another ring "bucket" on the drive chain.

The cure: a small guard rail in just the right place

A CURE FOR SPITTING

A small strip of metal is all it took to cure the clock of spitting weights, but it took months to detect the cause of the problem.

Not until a whole hour later would the pinwheel mechanism come back around again and flick the off switch. Saunders was getting worried. No matter what he did, the balls kept dropping! In desperation, our horological hero took a step back and looked at the larger picture.

A Tricky Fix

Inside what Saunders calls the "top cube" of the clock case—the part with the clock faces—there is a frame that holds up the clockwork mechanisms. At its lowest point, this frame is only two inches from the malfunctioning cross-ramp and guardrail.

A tiny piece of brass (screwed to the bottom of the frame at the midpoint of the cross-ramp and extending down a little more than an inch) was enough to block the bearings, stopping their dropping and guiding them on a straight and narrow path to the drive chain. With a little trial and error (remember Burt's method?), Saunders worked out the best size and positioning for his brass ball-bearing blocker. There! Better than ever.

A Repair Budget

The steam clock soldiered on for more than a year after the car accident while the machinery of Vancouver meshed with that of ICBC and ICBC's contribution for the accident damage was settled (only $2,000). In October of 2002, after the tourist high season, everything finally came together for a restoration project. For reasons unknown (but almost certainly related to the enormous popularity of the Gastown Steam Clock and its importance as a tourist draw), political will and bureaucratic support meshed and a budget was approved to bring the celebrity timepiece back into the pink of health. It even included some long-awaited items, like recognizing the contributing sponsors and donors.

The Information Plaques

The original plan called for four bronze information and recognition plaques: the dedication plaque, the steam clock information plaque, the Gastown history plaque, and the sponsor plaque. They are attached, one per side, to the upper base cube (which holds all the electrical innards) and give hints of Gastown's and the steam clock's picturesque histories.

Notice

Restorations Work By Ray Saunders and Ornamental Bronze Ltd.

The Gastown Steam Clock is temporarily out of service due to a motor vehicle accident. The repairs are expected to be completed by the end of February, 2003. We apologize for the inconvenience.

The City of Vancouver and the Gastown Business Improvement Society

PUBLIC NOTICE

Sign placed in the clock while the repair project was organized, the budget approved, and the repairs effected. It took months.

Local politics, economic cycles, changing social values, human tragedies and triumphs, an engineering rule ignored, and human spirit triumphant: all the elements that make life exciting.

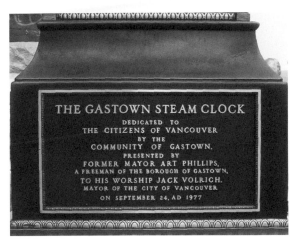

DEDICATED TO ...

A gift for the people of Vancouver, given by the people and businesses of Gastown

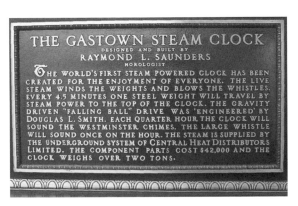

A NICE TRY BUT ...

It skips over most of the fascinating facts in the steam clock's history.

THE SPONSOR PLAQUE

The sponsor plaque was part of the original plan to acknowledge major contributions. Unfortunately, at the time the clock was ready for the plaque, fundraising was going rapidly only from a snail's perspective. Consequently, this relatively minor expense ran up against the ongoing cash drought. Since donations were still being sought, more sponsors were expected to step up to the plaque.

The casting process is five steps: First, make an aluminum model or "blank" of the finished plaque. Second, squirt the desired text, names of the sponsors in this case, on the aluminum blank with resin. Third, press the engraved aluminum model into very fine sand to make a mould. Fourth, pour molten bronze into the mould to create the unfinished bronze plaque. And fifth, smooth, coat, and polish and you're done. They were stuck at the second step. The bronze plaque could not be cast until the hoped-for dollars materialized and fundraising ceased.

What to do? Ornamental Bronze Ltd., the foundry casting the plaques, graciously loaned their aluminum blank, embellished with a simple "Contributors." Saunders fixed the aluminum plate to the clock and the "temporary" sponsor plaque was in place for the unveiling in 1977—and for twenty-five years thereafter!

The fundraising did not continue and eventually the fundraising committee dissolved. The need for donations to fund the bronze sponsor plaque was aired on TV and mentioned in Saunders's proposals to the city for steam clock improvements. But with Saunders's focus turned to other projects, the situation got too little attention to stir any response from either city officials or the donating public. So, year after year, when city budgeting priorities were shuffled and the cards dealt, the sponsor plaque item would turn up in the discard pile.

While planning the repairs after the car accident, in the general mood of goodwill and perhaps some political opportunism, room was found in the budget to repair and renovate the local marvel. And, lo and behold, a quarter century after the steam clock was commissioned, slipped in amongst the larger items was funding for a bronze sponsor plaque!

STEAM DAMAGE

Some of the clock's innards on Saunders's work table, awaiting refurbishment

A Reno

The steam clock was completely disassembled, repaired, cleaned, refinished, polished, and burnished before being reassembled and recommissioned. The aluminum model of the finished plaque was detached and returned to Ornamental Bronze. The base cube was removed and repaired, dial-light fixtures were changed, and a steam solenoid valve was replaced. A hot air exhaust fan was added to the

HOW THE HECK?

Replacing a corroded vent bolt reveals treasures (75¢ plus memorabilia). But the vents slant down, so how did they get inside?

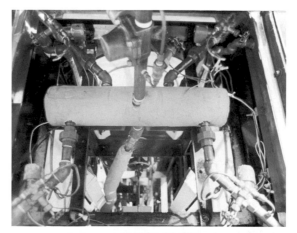

STEAM TO THE WHISTLES

The original steam manifold allowed condensation to form in the pipes, which then sprayed hot water on everyone nearby when the next time tune played.

roof vents, and improvements were made to the weight loading and unloading system. Interior brass trim and accent lighting were added.

A lever and a support rod were added to the donor plaque access panel and the main side panel door respectively.

Meanwhile, at Ornamental Bronze, names of the major sponsors were applied and molten metal was poured into the mould to complete a bronze sponsor plaque. Names of the many donors who gave smaller amounts were engraved on sheets of brass to serve as a finishing touch to the interior corners of the case.

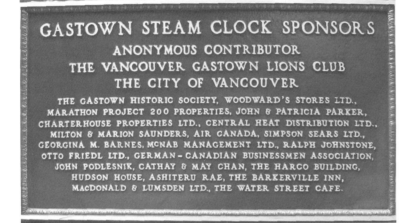

THE SPONSOR PLAQUE

The bronze version does look better than aluminium.

ENGRAVED IN BRASS 1

Names of smaller donors decorate an inside corner of the clock case, concealing pipes and wires.

ENGRAVED IN BRASS 2

The names are in no discernable order.

ENGRAVED IN BRASS 3

One set of names conceals wires.

ENGRAVED IN BRASS 4

One set of names conceals a drain pipe.

So, by concealing a steam pipe in one, wiring in another, and drain pipes in the remaining two corners, the givers are still giving.

Subsequently, in October of 2002, after a delay of just twenty-five years and a few days, the original plan to recognize contributors was finally implemented. The Sponsor Plaque was affixed forever to the restored base of a refurbished and gleaming Gastown Steam Clock.

Tuning the whistles turned out to be simpler.

TUNING TRIBULATIONS

An unhappy side effect of the 1977 seamstresses' strike threat arose from the method used to quell the revolt. You will recall that the obvious solution involved the immediate and permanent reduction of steam pressure to the whistles. To everyone's chagrin, like blowing on a tuba, inadequate pressure yields quiet but inadequate tonal qualities. On the instant, the steam clock whistle chimes went from loud and semi-tuneful all the way to sedate and discordant.

WHAT COMPLAINTS?

From the unveiling of the clock in 1977, Saunders, the Gastown Business Improvement Society, and City of Vancouver officials received hardly any objection to the discordant notes being played by the clock whistles. "Only one or two people would come into my shop in the course of a year and take issue with the discord," Saunders said. Of course, that did not mean the conflicting notes were enjoyable. This was another case of the squeaky wheel getting the grease. With so few complaints, Saunders focused his attentions on other aspects of the steam clock maintenance.

But still, what could justify taking a quarter of a century to tune the whistles? Saunders didn't know it would be easy to do! He wanted to have the whistle casings re-machined to be thinner and provide softer sounding tones (a good idea that he later implemented for the stainless steel steam clock in Indianapolis, Indiana). But that would require that the whistles go back to the factory to re-machine and retune the whole caboodle.

Saunders, mistakenly as it turned out, lumped tuning the existing whistles in with that larger remanufacturing process. He didn't twig that the two tasks could be separated.

When the accident repair and refurbishment project was underway, Erin Morgan, an acquaintance from The 50 Bourbon Street, a Gastown watering hole with an eclectic clientele, offered to help Saunders tune the whistles. She had noticed they were a bit out of

"THE WESTMINSTER CHIMES"

The music was inspired by a phrase from Handel's symphony *I Know That My Redeemer Liveth*. Words and music arranged in 1793 by the unfortunately named William Crotch.

Lord through this hour,

Be Thou our guide

So, by Thy power

No foot shall slide.

CENTRAL HEAT COMMITMENT

Central Heat committed to spending up to $1,500 per year on maintenance of the connection.

"It's 'more than enough' to keep it working. They have replaced the pressure-reducing valve occasionally over the years," Saunders reports, "but usually all it takes is a little adjustment when the whistles start going wonky."

tune. This was a nice euphemism. The discord was out of character for British Columbia. People from around the world must be embarrassed for us. Something had to be done!

PERFECT PITCH

Morgan, as it turned out, like the California Duo, was a street musician. She claimed that she could tune the whistles by ear! No whistle remanufacturing was required at all. Since sending the whistles back to the factory would not be happening any time soon, Saunders agreed to give it a try.

But this raises a question: How do you tune a clock's whistles? Carefully, as it happens, and with patient persistence.

Saunders opened the clock service door to give Morgan access to the tune machine, to show her how the system worked and what she had to do to make the whistles blow. Saunders climbed the scaffolding to reach the whistles, and removed the bell tubes (the outside shell of the whistles) so he could make the tuning adjustments as directed by Morgan.

Morgan crouched down and, reaching into the heart of the clock, tripped one of the five micro-switches causing the corresponding whistle to blow. She listened and then called out "up" or "down" to Saunders. Saunders turned the nut on the tuning rod to raise or lower it, as directed.

Morgan then pushed the tripping button, advancing the timing wheel and playing the next quarter-hour tune—making all the notes play—to hear if every note was now on pitch and in the same key. Going back to step three, Morgan advanced the micro-switch for the next whistle, and they repeated the tuning process until every note sounded right. That was it, the clock was tuned!

The entire process took Morgan and Saunders about an hour, and the clock whistles were in tune again for the first time since the steam pressure had been reduced! So the car accident precipitated a happier future for the steam clock and all its music-loving fans as the whistles were finally tuned, and finely tuned at that.

Except for the main whistle, which, still at 17 psi, manages only a ponderous, asthmatic wheeze. But by the time it sounds, "The Westminster Chimes" tune is complete, so no harm no foul, as they say in the music world (with apologies to sports fans everywhere).

It is a good thing, but benefits to visiting and local ears notwithstanding, this author confesses he misses the old, inebriated-clock sound. Go figure!

ADJUSTING TIME
Saunders makes adjustments to the timing.

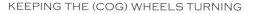

REPLACING PARTS

In 1977, every new part was another piece that didn't fit. And if it did fit the first time, it seemed like a lucky accident. To this day, getting things to fit can be a challenge. In the summer of 2006, for example, the tune machine—a mechanical delight—was getting long in the tooth and not so reliable. It was decided to install new circuit breakers and a waterproof container complete with a computerized tune controller as a replacement. As well, a replacement chain was donated by Renolds Canada, as the old windup chain was rusty.

The chain had arrived and other approving, organizing, and budgeting delays were finally overcome. City engineer Chris Homewood fenced the clock off and opened it up to install the computer controller in place of the old tune machine.

Saunders was also on hand to give the clock another good going-over, and to replace the chain. But it wouldn't fit! The links in the chain turned out to be too big for the sprockets. Again, serendipity saved the day as the right size of chain turned up just blocks away at a local supplier. It was also cheap enough not to wreck the maintenance budget, which was serendipity working overtime.

A Chain Reaction

Actually replacing the chains, however, is not for the untrained or faint-hearted. To replace the lift or drive chain, you must first ensure the replacement chain is the correct length. One at a time, attach the weight "buckets" to links spaced along the chain. Three-quarters of a small hoop made from an eighth-inch-thick brass rod, a bucket is about a half inch smaller in diameter than the ball-bearing weight it is designed to transport. Quickly remove buckets as required and re-attach them so they all face in one direction.

Now, putting these things on the cogwheels is sort of like threading a needle while clipping your cat's claws. You have to get it just right.

Hold the chain up so it doesn't tangle. Now loop it over the upper cogwheel by twisting yourself halfway into the clock waist. Reach around and past the steam engine and up and behind the supporting brackets attached to the clockworks; strain to lift the heavy chain—it's like a bicycle chain, only the links are bigger and it weighs more. Don't worry, the glass window is shatterproof. Watch your knuckles.

Now you're holding one end of the chain in your right hand so it won't run off the upper cogwheel, pulled by its own weight. If you let go, it will drop down below the steam engine support frame in

THE TUNE WHEEL

The brass pegs on the tune wheel activate solenoids on the right as the wheel turns. The solenoids release steam via a manifold under the roof to the whistles up above.

UPGRADE!

Chris Homewood, sidewalk superintendent and city engineer in charge, observes as the clock is rewired for a new control box.

behind the new electrical panel. The electrical panel and tune machine and steam fittings all reside in the bottom cube, so it's crowded down there. Reaching in and under the panel to get behind and retrieve a dropped chain is a pain and a half.

You've set one hand to holding the top end of the chain and the other hand to holding the bottom end. Otherwise the bottom end will dangle and you won't be able to reach it to pull up and around the bottom cogwheel (which, you'll find, is also in your way).

So, you hold the bottom end, and twisting yourself into a pretzel, you cram your right arm between yourself and the windows, head craning forward past your shoulder, and fold the other hand in beside you, wrist cocked. Grip the chain (hopefully with a good, tight grip because this chain is pretty heavy) and try to loop the bottom end of the chain down and around onto the bottom cogwheel (keep the top end straight so it doesn't pop off).

When you get it on, you will invariably move your top hand as you try to back out of your own way, and pull the chain off the upper cogwheel. In trying to loop that back on, you will lose your grip and the chain will drop and you will have to start all over. This will happen a number of times while you develop the necessary skill.

Eventually, you will have a hand on each end, the chain in place and pulled taut, ready for the connecting link to be inserted. This is when you realize you need another hand. After the panic subsides, you carefully put both chain-ends in one hand. Let's assume you have a good grip.

Your nose will start to itch. Zen deep within, going past the itch to the reason for the itch—and turn it off. Now reach for the little link that does the job of holding the ends together: the connecting link. You will discover it's out of your reach.

If you don't have a helper handy to reach under your right armpit to pick up and place the connecting link in your hand … well, you have to let go and watch it all drop down to the bottom again. Retrieve it and this time put a piece of wire through the top end link first, and start again—again.

Now, at long last, with your back screaming and your right shoulder on its last legs, so to speak, carefully grip both ends of the chain in one hand. Now dexterously thread the wire from the top link through the bottom end link and cinch it up. Whew!

Take a moment to convolute your body out of the clock case, stretch luxuriously and work the kinks out. Now prepare to twist back into the clock waist, because you're still not done. But first, carefully set the connecting link and the tiny spring clip that holds it in place where A) you can reach and B) they won't fall to the bottom.

COMPUTERIZATION

A new power box and programmable tune control (circled)—exciting for programmers

CHAIN DUCKS

The chain-changing ducks are all in a row.

A NEW CHAIN

Saunders gets organized to swap out the old worn chain for one donated by Renolds PLC, which produces industrial chains and related power transmission products.

REPLACING CHAIN

Replacing the chain is awkward to say the least—it's crowded in there.

PERSPECTIVES

A steam clock's life is never straight up and down. It comes complete with a certain amount of angularity.

Step C) is to find and pick up the link and clip and put them in a different place where you can't knock them off. Stretching halfway into the case, with the wire taking up much of the weight of the chain, pull the ends tight. Grip the end links in one hand and push, wiggle, and jiggle until the link pin is all the way through them. Next, put the tiny spring clip over the pin ends, with your sausage fingers, to hold the connecting link in place. Finally, remove that lifesaving piece of wire and you're done!

So you see, there's nothing (much) to it.

A TARGET

Once the steam clock became recognized and popular around the world, it became a target for engineers, maintenance workers, sidewalk superintendents, and armchair artists. To them, it had to be made more efficient, easier to service, more reliable. To others it wasn't accurate, it was too loud or an eyesore or a waste of money … the list of criticisms grew. Despite this constant attack from the terminally practical, the Gastown Steam Clock remained magical and mystical. Then the devil showed up, under the guise of common sense, agitating for changes to reduce the maintenance budget on the one hand but refusing to pay for maintenance-reducing capital improvements on the other.

For example, Saunders proposed a two-cylinder version of the steam engine boasting an automatic on/off feature that would have reduced the always-on wear and tear considerably. It would turn on when all the weights were at the bottom, send them all back up, and then turn off again. But the city said an emphatic no to the nearly $12,000 cost.

So, gradually, the electric motor took on more of the weight-lifting responsibilities (the steam engine failed with increasing frequency) until, sometime in the fifth year of operation, the steam supply to the engine was disconnected. The steam engine was reduced to an exhibit, driven by the concealed electric motor—like a preserved heart with a pacemaker on display in a pathology lab. Yes, it is a great insult but electricity powers the steam engine, turning the chain-drive that lifts the ball-bearing weights.

Today, steam blows the clock's steamboat-like whistles, electricity powers the lift chain, gravity powers the drive chain that keeps the pendulum in motion, and the Gastown Steam Clock is a steam-electric-gravity clock, to be precise. That's not bad, but not what was envisioned. Anyone got a maintenance-free baby steam engine? Here's a chance to make history.

There Is Magic!

There is a new genre in popular writing and entertainment—steam punk. The Gastown Steam Clock is a precursor of this new fascination with old technology. It is mysterious, quirky, and gorgeous. But the quality at its heart is a three-letter word: FUN.

Weights are carried up, roll across, then drop, supplying power to the pendulum; the mechanical complexities seize your attention! The pendulum swings, ticking and tocking. More power makes the ticks and tocks louder, but it moves not one bit faster! The length of the pendulum determines the speed at which it swings in cooperation with gravity. They're a team, and there is magic in that.

In the gradual process of improving reliability and reducing maintenance costs, the clock is changing—and losing some of its steam punk character. Electricity now drives the steam engine, turning the drive wheel and pushing the piston rod back and forth, which is all backwards for steam pistons. The tune machine was ripped out, driving more magic from the world. Its replacement is a program on a computer chip, all its bits on or off, one or zero, black or white: no grey left, no two or three, no half on half off. What is there Edwardian about a computer? A Babbage Difference Machine, which is a mechanical wonder—now that would work.

STUART TURNER #4
The steam engine actually powered the lift chain for about five years, but now holds an honourary position, like a Canadian senator.

A Different Approach

The clock is fascinating because it is a mechanical fantasy—not because it is efficient and never needs human attention to keep working. The reduction in its gadgetry quotient has produced a corresponding reduction in romantic charm. The future could see the trend reversed.

It would take vision, enthusiasm, a touch of renewed dedication, and a public recognizing that the Gastown Steam Clock does not ttract visitors by the busload because it is an accurate and reliable representation of the time of day. They travel to Vancouver from down the street and around the world to be educated, titillated, fascinated, and amused—and to experience the quirky mechanical masterpiece of street art known as the Gastown Steam Clock.

Money doesn't need to be an issue. Organizations like the Gastown Business Improvement Society, the Vancouver Tourist Bureau, Tourism British Columbia, and others are budgeted to encourage and support business in general and tourism in particular. Target some of that attention on a proven crowdpleaser.

THE GASTOWN BOB
There's gold at the end of that thar hickory pendulum! Bob weighs 42 pounds, and if it were solid gold it would be worth over a million dollars today. But don't get excited! It's solid cast iron inside a fraction of an ounce of gold leaf to make it look pretty.

SLAVES TO TIME

Saunders would love to put these time workers to the task of maintaining the Gastown Steam Clock.

TIMEWORKERS

Above: The Steam Engineer keeps things running smoothly.

Below: The Ball Bearing Worker just keeps things running.

Let's return steam power to the steam clock: replace the old steam engine with a nice new twin-cylinder Victoria model and add a new, old tune machine. Implement a few of Saunders's other whimsical gadget ideas and increase Vancouver's magic quotient. Let's make the world a happier place.

VISION FOR THE FUTURE

Ray Saunders remembers fondly the ambience and energy created by street musicians plying their trade beside the clock. Street vendors and entertainers were outlawed near the clock, presumably to reduce traffic congestion and perhaps panhandling.

High on the list of changes he would most like to make to the steam clock are special lighting for the Christmas season and better internal lighting. His desire from the start has been to add bronze statuettes: time workers engaged in whimsical tasks, for example a worker cleaning glass with a squeegee, a technician adjusting the time, an oiler lubricating the chain, and an inventory clerk counting the balls as they go by. What a great idea!

BY THE WAY

SCULPTURE BY R. L. SAUNDERS

Made of leftover bronze shavings
and bits and mounted on a slab
of Fraser River jade

By the Way

Steam travels through an underground network of pipes from a natural gas–fired steam-generating plant tucked under the escarpment east of Vancouver's downtown core. Steam for the clock is taken from one of those pipes.

Appropriately named, Central Heat Distribution Limited provides heat and power to over 30 million square feet in more than 190 buildings in Vancouver. The company is a privately owned district energy utility with a typical Vancouver-style history.

The Beginnings of Steam in Gastown

The city was booming in the sixties, but along with the attendant industrial and commercial buildings came stand-alone boilers with coal- and oil-burning furnaces. These, added to the ranks of the forest industry's beehive waste-wood burners scattered in and around the city, spewed copious amounts of pollutants. Not surprisingly, air quality was suffering.

At an informal lunch, local business people gathered to discuss the growing air pollution problem. These were decisive people with access to substantial financial resources. When Dave Leaney, president of D. W. Thomson, a local engineering firm, said, "I know what we can do," they listened to his suggestion for a district energy utility. Leaney had lots of credibility, and before lunch was over there was a collective "sounds like a good idea; let's do it." Life was simpler then.

Jon Ellis's original idea for a steam device evolved from a meeting between Ellis and Jim Barnes, then president of Central Heat. In addition to having Central Heat provide steam to the clock, Barnes had employees Phil Doran, Dave Falcon, Ralph Johnstone, and Johnny Podlesnick construct the underground connections and controls, help test the whistles, and eventually hook it all up on installation day.

John Barnes, the son of Jim Barnes, is now president and general manager of Central Heat. Barnes is pleased by the success of the steam clock, saying it is "a boost for the city, a community anchor point, and one of the most photographed things in the city."

STEAM MAINTENANCE

A Central Heat technician works on the steam supply connection to the manifold.

CENTRAL HEAT

"We help our customers reduce costs for heating and cooling their buildings and running steam-powered equipment, steam ironing in laundries, for example…. By replacing pairs of low-pressure boilers with a heat exchanger, we eliminate the need for smoke stacks, free up floor space, reduce heat loss, and offer more reliable and flexible power at lower cost while leaving more space for public use and making a smaller impact on the environment."

– John Barnes

CLOCK COMPLEXITIES

Most people have no idea just how tricky and complex mechanical clocks are. They are full of oddities like "escapements" and "jewels" and a "pendulum" with a "bob." Does this all sound familiar? Try this one: How does the coefficient of expansion and "Invar" affect clock function? You may know about the coefficient of expansion, but you've never heard of Invar—unless you're a metallurgical engineer, an avid clock collector, or the trivia ruler of the universe. For everyone else, here's a quick Invar[1] summary.

Moisture in the air and changes in temperature affect the length of a pendulum. If the pendulum expands, the tick-rate slows—and time appears to slow (the clock falls behind standard time). If the pendulum shrinks, the tick-rate speeds up—and time appears to speed up (the clock gets ahead of standard time).

Invar is a nickel-steel alloy that doesn't shrink or expand when the humidity or temperature changes, as do other metals and to a lesser extent wood. An Invar pendulum's *ticks* and *tocks* are the same under all atmospheric conditions—so the clock it regulates tells time consistently and, if you set it right to start with, accurately.

That is, as long as all of the many other parts of the clock's workings are in good shape. It takes skill to get a clock to work at all and dedication to keep it accurate.

Saunders ordered an Invar pendulum for the Gastown Steam Clock, only Gillett & Johnston couldn't find any at the time. But Burt and his method work in England too, helping them come up with a solution—hickory wood—which does a decent job and was cheaper. Problem solved, and to this day the hickory pendulum drives the steam clock's escapement mechanism.

THE BEAUTY OF A PENDULUM

The mechanism delivering power is a set of moving chains. The lift chain elevates ball bearings to the top of the chain loop where they drop off and roll down a short trough to the gravity chain, which carries them to the bottom where they roll back to their starting point at the lift chain and do it again, ad infinitum. The gravity chain provides the impetus needed to keep the pendulum swinging, thereby driving the clockworks.

Uneven or unreliable power would, one might think, make for an inconsistent and at best approximate display of the time. Not so, says Saunders. Excess power would make the clock tick louder but not go faster. The beauty of a pendulum is that the speed at which it

TESTING THE STEAM

Saunders makes sure Central Heat's steam supply works effectively to blow a test whistle.

moves (period of motion) is controlled by the length of the rod and the weight of the bob. Poetic and seemingly counterintuitive, but that's the way it works—and why invention of the pendulum clock produced the first really accurate timekeeping mechanism. (Period of motion is determined by the length of the rod from its hinge to the centre of gravity of the bob attached at the other end. The weight of the bob actually reduces variations caused by external influences like friction, air resistance, fluctuations in gravity, and flapping butterfly wings.)

Eleven!

That's the number of steam clocks extant in the world—as revealed by English web searches. There may be more, hiding out behind other languages, but not very many.

Steamy descendants of the Gastown Steam Clock, built by our redoubtable horologist Ray Saunders, number four. The Otaru Clock in Otaru, Japan, is a copy of the Gastown Steam Clock with some planetary additions. The Intrawest Resort Clock is a tower clock in Whistler, British Columbia. The Station Steam Clock, in a mall in Coquitlam, British Columbia, celebrates the importance of time to train schedules and steam locomotives. Finally, the only known stainless steel steam clock resides in front of the Indiana State Museum in Indianapolis, Indiana. Saunders has one more, his sixth, in the works for a tourist attraction in Katoomba, Australia, at this writing. Katoomba will be better known once it gets that steam clock.

Other Steam Clocks

Other fascinating steam clocks we have discovered that are worthy of note include:

In the United States, a towering steam-driven carillon clock tower, the Lansing Rotary Steam Clock, in Lansing, Michigan, and the Market Square Steam Clock at The Villages, Lake Sumter Landing, Florida.

In Great Britain, the Jersey Steam Clock, modelled on the historical Ariadne steamboat, resides on the Isle of Jersey. In Australia, a gorgeous, four-metre, all glass-encased steam clock stands in the Village of Berwick, City of Casey, Victoria.

Even defunct steam clocks are few in number. There are the Altoona Steam Clock, a smokestack-like tower in Altoona, Pennsylvania, and the inventive Neal's Yard Steam Clock in Chelsea Farmer's Market, London, England.

HANGIN' ROUND ...
The pendulum with its bob, ready to swing into action.
A knurled nob below the bob winds it up or down to adjust the period of motion and hence the duration of the clock's seconds.

MARKET SQUARE STEAM CLOCK

... was donated by the Lake Sumter Landing Businessman's Association. It has two large pistons in the waist of the clock and hisses through its hourly routine.

ROTARY CLUB INTERNATIONAL

Founded in 1905 by a group of Chicago businessmen "rotating" meetings in their offices, that small club grew into a service organization with more than 1.2 million business and professional members in 33,000 clubs worldwide. The Rotary Club of Lansing was established in 1916.

Members work to combat hunger, improve health and sanitation, provide education and job training, promote peace, and eradicate polio under the motto "Service Above Self."

Rotarians are guided by the answers to four simple questions:

Is it the truth?

Is it fair to all concerned?

Will it build goodwill and better friendships?

Will it be beneficial to all concerned?

ROTARY STEAM CLOCK

Donated in 1997 by the Rotary Club of Lansing, Michigan, this tower clock plays a wide range of tunes with an automatic music system replicating forty-nine carillon bells and a harp bell.

THE ALTOONA STEAM CLOCK

In Altoona, Pennsylvania, this very tall steam clock commemorates the area's proud history as a railroad waypoint.

STEAM CLOCK FASCINATION

Clocks play a big, even central, role in our lives. They help us manage how we use our allotted time: for commitments and responsibilities as well as our relationships and the events of our lives. In truth, clocks are a fundamental tool for effective living.

But why the Gastown Steam Clock holds such fascination for people is known only to the Great Clockmaker in the sky. Is it human fascination with mechanical marvels, or the equally strong allure of steam power and nature's ability to turn water into steam in the first place? Maybe the mystery is itself the hook.

THE ARIADNE

At the top of the hour, the paddlewheels turn, the waters boil, and steam pours from the funnels. Representing one of the original steamers sailing the England-Channel Islands route, the Ariadne can be found behind the Maritime Museum in St. Helier on the Island of Jersey.

PETER WEARE'S CREATION

This Australian original suffered from natural weathering and extensive vandalism in its original park setting and had to be moved to a more secure location.

NEAL'S YARD STEAM CLOCK

Built by Tim Hunkin and Andy Plant in 1984, this incredible construct no longer steams but remains as a feature of the farmer's market in Chelsea, London, England. See a descriptive poster at http://www.timhunkin.com/86_steamposter.htm

Whatever the reasons, the measurement and nature of time have proven endlessly fascinating to those of us caught up in it, which is to say everyone. Time has captured the attention of many great thinkers as well: Stephen Hawking, Albert Einstein, St. Thomas Aquinas, to name but a few.

In fact, on perusing the history of timekeeping technology, one quickly discovers that the clocks and watches we take for granted today have a tradition and legacy that is nothing short of astounding. Clock and watch technology was the concrete expression, for the better part of five millennia, of leading-edge scientific thinking and manufacturing technology. Celestial bodies were the focus for thousands of years—telling time by the season—resulting in artifacts like Stonehenge and, at the small end, sundials.

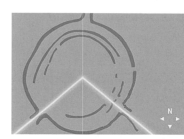

THE GOSECK CIRCLE

Sunrise and sunset at the winter solstice are in yellow. The faint vertical line is the meridian.

GOSECK PALISADES

To preserve an authentic look, the wooden palisades of the Goseck Circle were reconstructed using hand tools.

NEWGRANGE

This prehistoric site predates the Great Pyramid of Giza in Egypt by over 500 years and most Stonehenge constructs by about 1,000 years.

AVEBURY CIRCLE

This site is a popular spiritual centre for modern day Pagans, Wiccans, and Druids.

SOME ASTRONOMICAL ICONS

GOSECK CIRCLE—NEOLITHIC CIRCA 4900 BC

Located in Saxony-Anhalt, Germany, the Goseck Circle, the best preserved of over 250 ring-ditches known in Eastern Europe, changed our understanding of history. The site was first identified by aerial photography of crop marks in a wheat field in 1991. Excavation began in 2002. Now the earliest known sun observatory in the world, it revealed that more accurate astronomy, and hence time measurement, existed in Europe than was previously believed.

Postholes from the original and discarded potsherds tell the Goseck story. When a post rots, the posthole gradually fills with sediments, leaving a readily discernible pattern for archeologists. Bits of pottery found at the site bore patterns known to have been made as early as 4900 BC, showing an age just shy of 7,000 years!

At the winter solstice, sunrise and sunset could be seen through the southeast and southwest gates respectively. The Goseck Circle allowed coordination of lunar and, more difficult, solar calendar measurements, apparently in a spiritual context.

With no evidence of fire or other damage, why the site was abandoned is a mystery. On the winter solstice, December 21, 2005, the site was opened to the public.

NEWGRANGE—CIRCA 3100 BC

Near Drogheda, County Meath, north of Dublin, Ireland, Newgrange is the most famous Irish prehistoric site. Newgrange was built so that at dawn of the winter solstice, the shortest day of the year, for a very short time a narrow beam of sunlight illuminates the floor of the cross-shaped chamber at the end of a sixty-foot-long passageway.

AVEBURY—CIRCA 3000 BC

In Wiltshire, England, Avebury contains a large henge (a flat oval area surrounded by a ditch and bank earthworks) and several stone circles. One of the largest Neolithic monuments in Europe, it is older than the nearby Stonehenge megaliths (thirty-two kilometres away).

STONEHENGE—FIRST EARTHWORKS CIRCA 3100 BC; MEGALITHS CIRCA 2500 BC

Also in Wiltshire, near Amesbury and north of Salisbury, England, Stonehenge might be the best known of all prehistoric monuments. A typical earthwork surrounds the iconic monument.

With cremated remains dating from 3000 through 2500 BC, Stonehenge takes centre stage in a region that includes several hundred burial mounds and other prime examples from the Neolithic Age and the Bronze Age.

STONEHENGE

Made of large standing stones, of which some were erected as early as 3000 BC, some as much as 900 years later

CALLANISH—CIRCA 2000 BC

Located on the Isle of Lewis in the Outer Hebrides of northwest Scotland, the village of Callanish juts out into Loch Roag, about twenty-one kilometres west of Stornoway (administrative centre of the Outer Hebrides).

The Callanish Stones are a cross-shaped setting of standing stones, the most remarkable such monument in Scotland. The circle was buried in a peat bog until 1857.

CALLANISH STONES

The central stone is sixteen feet high and is encircled by thirteen smaller stones.

DROMBEG STONE CIRCLE—LATE NEOLITHIC/ EARLY BRONZE AGE

Southwest Ireland contains about fifty stone circles including one of the most popular megaliths in Ireland. The Drombeg Stone Circle, east of Glandore in County Cork, is a recumbent stone circle thought to have been used for lunar observations and marking the changing seasons.

The long recumbent is flanked by portal stones with a southwest orientation. It lines up with the setting sun through a distant notch in the hills during the midwinter solstice.

DROMBEG STONE CIRCLE

Known also as The Druid's Altar, of seventeen original stones thirteen survive.

TOWERS OF CHANKILLO—400 BC

Chankillo is an ancient complex in the coastal desert of Peru, built around 400 BC. The ruins of a fortified temple, plus gathering places and residential areas, lie near a solar observatory.

Its thirteen towers stretch three hundred metres north to south along a low hill ridge. From two observation points along the horizon, evenly spaced narrow gaps in the towers correspond closely to sunrise and sunset positions over the course of a year.

TOWERS OF CHANKILLO

Remains of the Chankillo fortress on a hilltop near the observatory

TIMELY INFLUENCES

Over the centuries, everybody got into the act, finding ingenious methods and building quirky structures to measure the passage of time. Indeed, time proved to be a dimension where art, science, and technology could meet and where creative genius could flourish.

SUNDIALS

NIL SINE NOBIS

Sundial in the courtyard at Hôtel de Cluny (Musée National du Moyen Âge) in Paris, France. The work is from the Middle Ages. "Nil sine nobis" is Latin for "Nothing without us."

An educated guess places the first sundials around 3500 BC in Egypt or elsewhere in the Middle East. By the first century BC, they were everywhere in Rome, in both public squares and private courtyards. A Roman chronicler, Vitruvius, listed thirteen kinds of sundials in the city at that time.

Babylonians contributed to the measurement of time. Modern measures of 60 seconds, 60 minutes, and 360 degrees are inherited from the Babylonian sexagesimal counting system (base 60). An early Egyptian contribution was the shadow clock, a T-shaped device that, when held perpendicular with the crossbar aligned toward the sun, cast a shadow on the ruled vertical post to measure the time.

The twenty-four-hour day was also inherited from Egypt, where daylight and night were each divided into twelve equal parts. An hour of fixed duration was a later modification. Fixed interval time units weren't new, though. Other early "high tech" innovations like sand clocks and hourglasses, slow-burning candles with evenly spaced notches, the more famous sundials, and water clocks all used them.

SUNDIAL

Not as easy as it looks: the gnomon must be aligned to true (not magnetic) north and have its top edge (the style) at an angle from the horizontal that equals the number of degrees of latitude it is from the equator.

WATER CLOCKS

If you replaced the sand in an hourglass with water, you would have a simple water clock. A bucket with a hole in it would do too—with markings inside correlating the water flow-rate to chosen time units. Water clocks came into use around 1700 BC. They were called clepsydras by the ancient Greeks, meaning variously "water thieves" or "a stealer of water." They couldn't have been maintenance-free though, as they needed constant refills and cleaning of algae buildup: one can imagine some stand-up comedian in an old toga making apologies for being three water lilies and a bullfrog late for his dentist appointment. More advanced clepsydras had overflow channels and automatic rewind (a steady flow of water into the vessel).

Water clocks became so much a part of Roman culture that when lawyers needed more time to argue their case, the term they used was "aquam dare" (add water). If the same lawyers ran off at the mouth, wasting time, it was "aquam perdere" (to lose water). In those days, a cloudy day, sunset, a forgetful moment, or a cold snap, amongst other natural events, stopped time, or at least the measurement of it.

A LEGACY OF ODDBALL CLOCKS

In the arena of public clocks, the oddballs have reigned supreme. There is an old and well-established tradition of building strange and marvellous constructs to tell the time. Water clock technology generated interesting gadgets from the time of Amenhotep I, Pharaoh of Egypt around 1500 BC, gadgets like armillary spheres, celestial globes, and moving orreries. The Tower of Winds, built by Andronikos of Kyrrhos, a Macedonian astronomer of note, introduced an air of *je ne sais quoi* to the marketplace of Athens in the first century BC.

Possibly the most elaborate water clock, a marvellous three-storey, water-driven creation, was built in Bianjing, China (now Kaifeng in Henan Province), by Su Sung, minister of punishments and the calendar expert to child emperor Chen Tsung. It was known as the Cosmic Engine, and like Saunders and his crew, Su Sung and Han Kung-lien, his chief designer, had to overcome a great deal of financial adversity before finishing their masterpiece in AD 1094 after an eight-year construction effort. Su Sung's clock tower was destroyed after just thirty-nine years by invading Tatars or political feuding—take your pick: there are conflicting histories.

CLEPSYDRA

In the Agora of Athens, a water clock was used to time the senators' speeches, which were limited to six minutes. Getting a point across in a convincing manner within the time limit became an art.

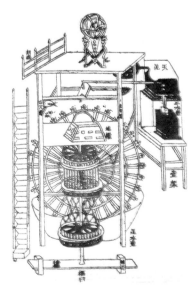

SU SUNG'S COSMIC ENGINE

This illustration of the inner workings and the armillary sphere of Su Sung's clock tower comes from his treatise published in the year 1092—over a thousand years ago. Upper and lower water reservoirs are shown on the right. Front and centre is the "earth horizon" box with its celestial globe on top. Below are left and right upper locks and balancing lever and a link to the upper reservoir. Below that are a timekeeping shaft and wheels resting in a mortar-shaped end-bearing. Behind is the main drive wheel with scoops at the end of the spokes.

A WATER CLOCK AND MORE

The Cosmic Engine's mechanism incorporated a water-driven escapement invented almost four centuries earlier, about AD 725.

The clock tower was over thirty feet tall, with another ten feet of observation platform that contained a large, waterwheel-powered, bronze armillary sphere for calendar and astrology observations.

A smaller star globe rotated in a lower chamber for observers who did not need to see the heavens. Five front panels had doorways that revealed shifting manikins, which not only rang bells or gongs but also held tablets indicating the hour or other special times of the day.

CHRISTIAAN HUYGENS

Creating the first working pendulum clock, apparently in his spare time, Huygens also discovered centrifugal force, was first to argue light consisted of waves, articulated the laws for collision of bodies, played a large role in the development of modern calculus, was first to write on the phenomenon of repetition pitch, explained Saturn's rings and discovered its moon Titan, created theoretical physics, and was one of the first to write science fiction!

COMPUT ECCLESIASTIQUE

A procession of life-size figures of Christ and the apostles occurs every day at noon clock time. The parade is repeated at midnight clock time.

The clock runs a half hour behind for some, surely a good, reason.

MECHANICAL ESCAPEMENTS

Water flow is irregular at best, and water clocks never achieved high accuracy. The search for greater precision led to weight-driven mechanical clocks. Their origins are uncertain, but they seem to have evolved around the turn of the first millennium AD, with the help of some prominent western religious figures. Pacificus, archdeacon of Verona, may have invented the first weight-driven clock in the ninth century AD, but nobody knows for sure. Pope Sylvester II may have invented a mechanical clock when still a lowly (but well educated) monk, around AD 996.

By the thirteenth century, mechanical escapements were in use in northern Europe, and relatively accurate timekeeping—regardless of the weather and light conditions—became common. Implementation of the new technology at that time was spearheaded by the church—to tell when it was time to pray, as is recalled by the word noon, which derives from Nones, the midday prayers. In those days, bells were used to signal the times (no numerals or hands yet). The word *clock* comes from the French for bell (*cloche*).

The beautiful Comput Ecclesiastique astronomic clock of Notre Dame Cathedral in Alsace, France, is a masterpiece first placed in the cathedral in 1352. It was rebuilt in the 1600s and replaced by a newer but similar version in the nineteenth century. It originally boasted elaborate mechanical devices such as a crowing cock, an even dozen apostles, a calendar dial, and an ingenious revolving celestial globe. The latest clock dates from 1843. It features the automata, a perpetual calendar with a computus, and a planetary dial (orrery); it displays the position of the sun, the moon, and eclipses of both.

GETTING TIME RIGHT

But in Europe, for everyday use, sundials remained the standard until lighter and smaller clocks could be made. Lighter and smaller became possible with the advent of spring-driven clocks in the early 1500s and pendulum clocks in the late 1600s.

A clockmaker in Nuremberg, Peter Henlein, appears to have invented spring-driven clocks in the early 1500s. Galileo apparently designed a pendulum clock as early as 1582, although he never built it. A Dutch scientist named Christiaan Huygens gets credit for actually building the first pendulum clock in 1656. With the pendulum came relatively accurate timekeeping, initially a one-minute loss per day, which Huygens eventually reduced to ten seconds per day.

Leading-edge clock technology and production capacity moved from China to Europe in the latter part of the first millennium AD, bounced around Europe for most of the second millennium, and then returned to the East (Japan) for a short while before spreading around the globe as it has in the past few decades. In an interesting aside, the technology of time was so important that industrial espionage seems to have played a rather large role in determining those movements—especially during Europe's millennium of leadership.

Lewis Mumford said, "[The clock] disassociated time from human events and helped create belief in an independent world of mathematically measurable sequences: the special world of science." He also advanced the notion that accurate timekeeping did more to enable the Industrial Revolution than steam power.

H1, H2, H3, AND THE H4

England enjoyed a period of glory as the empire and its navy expanded. Knowing where you were on the oceans of the world was quite tricky in those days, requiring a degree of accuracy in keeping track of the time relative to a fixed referent (originally the home port and eventually the Greenwich meridian) to determine a ship's longitude.[2]

An English carpenter, John Harrison, spurred by a huge reward of £20,000 offered by the British government in 1714, added a colourful chapter to the development of timekeeping technology. From 1730 until 1761, he worked to develop an accurate marine chronometer.

H1, H2, and H3, each about a metre on a side and weighing in at a hundred pounds or more, were his large-scale, traditional designs. He spent nineteen years on H3; but even with the addition of a revolutionary brass and steel bi-metallic strip to eliminate the effects of temperature changes, he couldn't get it reliable enough.

Designing a pocket watch as a tool to track the accuracy of the larger H3 took his mind in a different direction. Thinking small, he developed a model that was about five inches in diameter. The H4 was full of rubies and diamonds, which virtually eliminate friction, as well as a temperature-compensated mainspring. In a two-and-a-half-month sea trial, the H4 lost only five seconds!

England's Board of Longitude waffled on paying Harrison the £20,000 prize ($10,000,000 or more in current dollars) for developing an accurate naval chronometer. It took an appeal to King George III to get his well-earned reward. Harrison died three years after receiving the prize.

LEWIS MUMFORD 1895-1990

An American historian, renowned critic of literature and urban architecture, writer and philosopher, especially on technology and science and how it reshaped human society, Mumford didn't just practise his occupations; he changed the way people thought about them and about themselves. He said, "The clock is a piece of machinery whose 'product' is seconds and minutes."

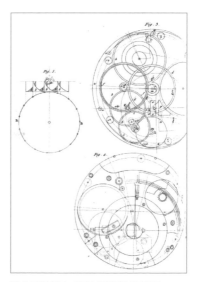

H4 NAVAL CHRONOMETER

Harrison H4 drawing from *The Principles of Mr. Harrison's Time-keeper 1767* by Ferdinand Berthoud, 1802.

The government got its money's worth: that edge in navigation is generally credited as a significant factor in Britain's rise to naval supremacy and in the expansion of the British Empire.

A CANADIAN IDEA

Unfortunately, the H4 didn't help anyone catch a train. On land, as rapid movement of goods and people was made possible by the steam engine, another sort of time challenge arose. Dawn, high noon, and nightfall don't happen at the same time everywhere. The resulting train-scheduling problems imposed a vexatious administrative burden and operational challenge as railroads expanded.

Sir Sandford Fleming, 1827–1915, was an engineer born in Scotland and raised in Canada. He proposed that the 360 degrees of longitude around the globe be divided into 24 time zones. The time would be the mean solar time at the central of the 15 meridians in each zone. Fleming proposed his solution at many conferences, first in 1879, only to have it pooh-poohed as a utopian, and hence impractical, vision. Persistence proved its worth, and in 1884 a modified version of his "Cosmic Time" was adopted at the International Prime Meridian Conference in Washington, D.C. At the same conference, the Greenwich meridian was accepted to be the prime meridian. While the specifics of his "Time Zones" were not officially adopted, over the next fifty years or so they were gradually implemented around the world.

SIR SANDFORD FLEMING (1827-1915)

Chief Engineer of the Canadian Pacific Railway, he is the father of the Standard Time system.

In 1876, a train schedule in Ireland had a misprint. As a result, a visiting Sandford Fleming missed a train. Sandford took umbrage at this: his response was to change the way the world measured time.

It's humbling to know this.

ELECTRICITY AND TIME

In contrast to this long and quite glorious history of horology, the computer and electronics technologies that are reshaping our world today have been a force for little more than eighty years.

In the late nineteenth century, technological development received a boost with the invention of electric clocks. In the 1930s and '40s, electric clocks proliferated for home use. Really accurate timekeeping did not arrive until 1927, when vibrating quartz crystals were incorporated into laboratory clockworks. But for the masses, the wider use of quartz clock technology had to await the development of cheap, semiconductor, digital logic in the '60s. Quartz clocks and watches remain the de facto standard for most timekeeping chores to the present day.

ATOMS TELL TIME

However, nuclear science brought timekeeping accuracy to new orders of precision with development of the atomic clock in 1948. Originally, ammonia atoms helped to reduce inaccuracies to one second in three thousand years. In 1999, a new time standard was set in the United States with a "fountain atomic clock." By observing a fountain of cooled caesium atoms tossed into the air by lasers, accuracy reached one second in twenty million years!

The US Naval Observatory (USNO) now has a rubidium clock in the works that will be 50 to 100 times more accurate than existing master clocks. The USNO's upper-case **M**aster **C**lock is backed up by almost 100 lower-case **m**aster **c**locks. Mostly caesium fountains, but including also hydrogen masers, they drive the GPS satellite network's positioning signals and contribute to the calculation of Coordinated Universal Time (UTC). The USNO contributes about forty per cent of the signals received from around the world, which are then weighted and averaged by the International Bureau of Weights & Measures outside Paris, to arrive at the UTC.

UTC has replaced GMT (Greenwich Mean Time) because the clocks are now more accurate than the earth at keeping time. To the purists, the earth's rotation is too irregular for accurate timekeeping. Besides, the rotation is actually slowing down, requiring adjustments be made that are not necessary with the new way of measuring. In 1967, the definition of second was changed from 1/86,400 of the mean solar day to 9,192,631,770 vibrations of a particular isotope of caesium.

TIME FICTIONS

And the language continues changing to reflect advances in time technology. Dan Falk, in his book *In Search of Time,* tells us that the word *chronoclasm* came into being as a label for the "intentional destruction of clocks and other time artefacts." In the online Urban Dictionary, however, the definition changes to "temporarily frazzled mental state resulting from the discovery that the actual time or date varies greatly from what you thought it was."[3]

THE FIRST SWISS QUARTZ CLOCK (on the left)

In 1927, Warren Marrison and J. W. Horton built the first quartz clock at Bell Telephone Laboratories.

Even the cheapest quartz wristwatch today gains or loses under a half second per day.

ATOMS & MICROWAVES

The principle of operation of an atomic clock is not based on nuclear physics, but rather on atomic physics and using the microwave signal that electrons in atoms emit when they change energy levels. Early atomic clocks were based on masers at room temperature. Currently, the most accurate atomic clocks first cool the atoms to near absolute zero temperature by slowing them with lasers and probing them in atomic fountains in a microwave-filled cavity. An example of this is the NIST-F1 atomic clock, the US national primary time and frequency standard.

The accuracy of an atomic clock depends on the temperature of the sample atoms—cooler atoms move more slowly, allowing longer probe times, and have reduced collision rates—and on the frequency and intrinsic width of the electronic transition. Higher frequencies and narrower lines increase precision.

CAESIUM FOUNTAIN CLOCK

A continuous cold caesium fountain atomic clock stands in a laboratory of the Swiss Federal Office of Metrology in Bern. FOCS 1 started operating in 2004 at an uncertainty of one second in 30 million years.

QUANTUM-LOGIC CLOCK

This experimental aluminum atom clock, a recent improvement by America's National Institute of Standards and Technology (NIST), will neither gain nor lose one second in about 3.7 billion years.

AND TIME FACTS

Enclosed in climate-controlled vaults, the USNO's Master Clock still broke down twice in the ten years leading up to 2007. Maybe the Gastown Steam Clock's record ain't so bad after all. Even these caesium and hydrogen maser clocks vary in their precision (by a few nanoseconds). Okay, the steam clock is not in the same class for accuracy. And now the University of Tokyo has designed a strontium "open lattice" clock that they say will only lose one second every thirty billion years.

I was good with one minute a day. If that still makes you feel rushed, try North Africa, where simple, metal clepsydras were still common in the twentieth century and where, if you look not too hard, you may find a place where they are still in use.

So, the humble clock and watchmakers of today were once the leading thinkers and highly paid technicians, as well as artists and artisans, of the Dark Ages and the Renaissance. And they were innovators, leading industrialists, and entrepreneurs until well into the twentieth century. Henry Ford, but one example, learned the basics of assembly-line production as a clockmaker.

With that kind of legacy, maybe it is not so surprising that the Gastown Steam Clock has captured the interest of engineers, horologists, collectors, modellers, and millions of sightseers of all ages. Unusual, surprising, ingenious, functional, attractive, impressive, and familiar all at once—the steam clock has it all. Perhaps instead of wondering at its popularity, we should wonder why anyone wonders why.

More About Ray Saunders's Clocks

At the start of 1974, Saunders had graduated from watch and clock repair technician (and a steady income) to struggling artist and entrepreneur. By the end of 1977, he was all of those things, but more than anything he was a designer and builder of innovative town clocks. He had found the passion that would demand his faithful, if divided, attention for the rest of his working life.

Besides the Gastown, Otaru, Whistler, Port Coquitlam, and Indianapolis steam clocks, Saunders's town clock portfolio includes a steamless copy of the Gastown Steam Clock in Yokohama, Japan, a moon clock in Richmond, B.C., a flower clock in North Vancouver, B.C., the Saunders Memorial Tower Clock in B.C.'s sunny Okanagan (commemorating Saunders's parents' contribution to the community of Penticton), and a host of smaller tower clocks and street clocks scattered far and wide.

Then there was the tower clock for a residential community just completed on Bear Mountain, near Victoria, B.C. There, the author, as Saunders's assistant, swung like a maladroit monkey on the tower construction scaffolding. We were five stories above the hard-packed ground, installing two eight-foot dials with synchronous, motor-driven clocks and self-lubricating (oil bath) drive mechanisms.

Saunders also repaired and upgraded a total curiosity, the Beast Clock, in Maple Ridge, B.C. A mechanical horse clock that rears to a height of forty feet, it was built by retired city employee Don Brayford. The bigger-than-life stallion rears up on its hind legs to celebrate the passing of every daylight hour.

DO BEARS TELL TIME?

The Bear Creek tower clock from inside the tower—bigger than the average bear.

NO RUST!

Created for the Indiana State Museum in 2002, this streamlined stainless steel beauty is seventeen feet high and plays "Back Home Again" (in Indiana) on eight brass whistles.

STEAM TRAIN CLOCK

A mall clock by Saunders in Port Coquitlam, B.C., celebrates the location's heritage as a stop on the nation-building CP Railway.

THE BEAST

A mechanical marvel located in Maple Ridge, B.C., created by Don Brayford in 1989—pictured under repair and refurbishment by Saunders at the turn of the millennium.

THE GASTOWN STEAM CLOCK

... will never grow up and still loves a party.

BIRKS CLOCK

Saunders restores the century-old clock from inside out. Try tying that to your wrist!

LUNAR CLOCK

A 1986 creation, Saunders states that it is The World's Largest Lunar Clock. The mall it centred failed and it now sits in a warehouse, awaiting a new home.

THE 2001 FLORAL CLOCK

Short-lived but gorgeous, it was 22 feet across and included a water feature (not shown).

At the other end of the clock spectrum, Saunders recently re-furbished the tower clock in Vancouver's City Hall and the famous (in Vancouver, at least) Birks Clock: a cast-iron sidewalk clock built for George Trorey Jewelers in 1906. It was renamed the Birks Clock when the firms amalgamated in 1907 and has been a trysting place for many a romantic couple ever since.

Presently working on a steam-engine clock for Scenic World in Katoomba, part of the Blue Mountain region near Sydney, Australia, he hasn't turned his back on the Gastown Steam Clock. In December of 2009, the city gave last-minute approval to a pro-posal from Saunders to refurbish the clock accents in time for the Winter Olympics and Paralympics held in Vancouver and Whistler in February and March of 2010. City engineer Chris Homewood, the city engineer responsible for the steam clock, was busy with 2010 Olympics-related projects, like the new Olympic Line tram service between Granville Island and the Olympic Village, and could not respond quickly to steam-clock service calls. So Saunders stepped into the breach and took first-responder duties again to ensure the Gastown Steam Clock kept on ticking.

PARALYMPICS 2010
Jennifer Pownall brings the Paralympic torch to the Gastown Steam Clock.

Scenic World Steam Clock
Katoomba, Australia

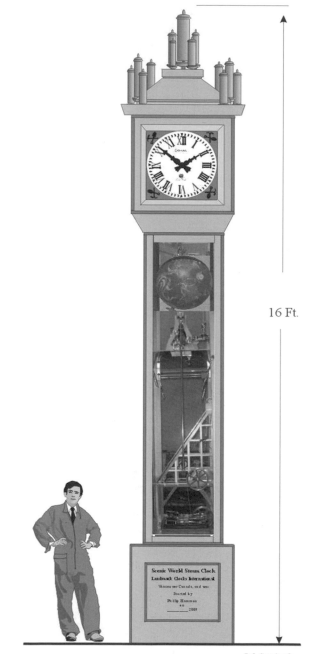

16 Ft.

R. J. Saunders ©

Features:

The twelve small brass whistles will play "Waltzing Matilda" each quarter hour. The large whistle will sound the hours.

Three Roman dials will be back-lit by LED lights and feature historic mining tools in each corner. A glass window at the back of the clock dial cube will allow visitors to view the workings.

A natural looking hand painted globe mounted on the clock works will feature LED lights marking major cities.

A bronze and stainless steel tower clock movement has a pinwheel escapement, and will drive the three clock dials.

The stainless steel case, with brass trim, has four long glass panels for viewing the interior clock features.

A unique incline weight drive system will power the clock movement. A model coal cart, filled with lead to looks like coal, provides the required force to power the clock movement.

A Twin Victoria model steam engine will wind up the coal cart, activated by two limit switches at the top and bottom of the track.

Descriptions of the clock's functions, whistle tune, Katoomba mining history, and dedication plaques will be mounted on the base cube.

NUMBER 12

The twelfth steam clock in the world and sixth made by Raymond Saunders will be installed at Katoomba in the Blue Mountains of Victoria, Australia. The current scheduled installation date is October 2011.

BACK MATTER

END NOTES

Quotations and facts that come from interviews with the author are not cited in these notes.

Web addresses cited were current at the time this book was published but may have changed.

CHAPTER 1

1   Members of The Town Group property developers in Gastown: Larry Killam, Howard Meakin, Bob Saunders, and Ian Rogers.

2   My friend and first reader Jennifer Pownall raises the disturbing question, "Isn't a sawmill a building?" The location of the mill is certainly part of Vancouver now, so the question is legitimate. Even if the area was not added to the city until later, it would seem to have some claim to "first building" status. The question won't be settled here.

3   From www.vancouverhistory.ca/archives. Information gleaned from the fascinating project of the late Vancouver writer/historian Chuck Davis, who started *The History of Metropolitan Vancouver*, a multi-year project reaching contributors and sponsors with the help of the internet. The book will cover the history of not only Vancouver but also the entire Lower Mainland region from 1827 to the present.

4   See www.vancouverhistory.ca/archives_kipling.htm for a fascinating anecdote of Rudyard Kipling's visits and speculation in, as Kipling phrased it, "Some four hundred well-developed pines, a few thousand tons of granite scattered in blocks at the roots of the pines, and a sprinkling of earth. That's a town lot in Vancouver."

5   The expression *Lotus Land* is undoubtedly rooted in Homer's *Odyssey*: land of lotus eaters. Variously described as a place or state of languid contentment or idyllic self-indulgence, the term was often used in the fifties and sixties to describe Vancouver and British Columbia by those living in harsher winter conditions and under more conservative social attitudes.

6   Joni Mitchell's hit song "Big Yellow Taxi" from her album *Ladies of the Canyon* released in 1970. Mitchell reportedly wrote this song her first time in Hawaii after opening her hotel room curtains and seeing beautiful green mountains in the distance. "Then, I looked down and there was a parking lot as far as the eye could see, and it broke my heart ... this blight on paradise. That's when I sat down and wrote the song."

7   There were no government-sanctioned business improvement associations (BIA). That was an import from the United States, courtesy of Jon Ellis. Gastown's BIA, the Gastown Business Improvement Society (GBIS), grew out of an on-again, off-again Gastown Merchants' Association and the Townsite Committee.

8   See Leonie Sandercock and Giovanni Attili, PIBC Keynote Speech, April 22, 2005.

9   Drawn primarily from the Townsite Committee, the Vancouver Gastown Lions Club, and the Gastown Merchants' Association, the Steam Clock Fundraising Committee as of July 15, 1977, comprised Doug Piepgrass, at that time president of the Vancouver Gastown Lions Club and promoter par excellence; Barry Shaw, who followed in the footsteps of Doug Piepgrass, becoming the next president of the Lions Club; Bill Woodruff from Woodward's Stores Ltd., which was a strong supporter and contributor to the steam clock; Jim Pollock, general manager of Town Shoes Ltd., who was a fundraising demon and deserves special mention for his commitment to the real fundraising work of canvassing, promoting, record keeping, and coordination (especially the second time around after the budget was increased to $42,000); and Jon Ellis of the City of Vancouver Planning Department, who was the instigator and even took a turn as the committee's chairman.

CHAPTER 2

1   This is apparently drawn from a movie about boxing wherein one character boxed using Burt's method, disdaining the Marquis of Queensbury rules, and regularly lost his fights as a result. Perhaps Saunders's use of the term is a maladaptation. Mike Spence reports that they would make a wire model of what was needed to develop an idea and test it with a more solid model before making the finished part—not as haphazard as it sounds.

2   This name variously spelled Thorston, Thorson, and Thorsen in Saunders's documents and clippings. Thorson seems to be the correct spelling.

3   The patterns served not only for the original Gastown steam clock, but for the Yokohama and Otaru (Japan) clock moulds as well. Thorson even made a spare set, another bit of good planning (or fortuitous impulse?) as it turns out. The spare became a wooden model of the clock for the Vancouver Airport, slightly downsized to fit the building. It was a feature in the international arrivals concourse for years and was subsequently purchased as an exhibit by an unfortunately short-lived Gastown enterprise called Storyeum: an interesting cross between a museum and a playhouse that provided a pay-for-getting-educated experience of local history.

4   The SS *Naramata* was launched in 1914, worked for fifty-three years, and now rests on the beach in Penticton beside the SS *Sicamous*. It is being restored as funds allow.

5   Not until an anonymous donor salvaged the steam clock project's finances could a copy of the whistle be made. The donor covered not only Saunders's unpaid bills and humble wages ($2.50 vs. the $3.50 minimum wage at the time and the $15 per hour paid to Doug Smith for his work), but also provided funds for a duplicate whistle. Hans Andriesse of Cannon Machine Works in Coquitlam remembers machining the copy for the steam clock from Bob Swanson's specifications. After nine months of yeoman-like service, the original whistle surrendered its time-telling duties and retired from the B.C. workforce once again—and Hobbis got his antique back with a colourful new chapter in its story.

CHAPTER 3

1   The hammered dulcimer is a stringed musical instrument with the strings stretched over a trapezoidal sounding board. Typically, the hammered dulcimer is set on a stand, at an angle, before the musician, who holds small mallet hammers in each hand to strike the strings.

The hammered dulcimer derives its name from the small mallets that players use to strike the strings, called *hammers*. Hammers are usually made of wood (most likely hardwood such as maple, cherry, padauk, oak, walnut, or any other hardwood), but can also be made from any material, including metal and plastic. "Hammered dulcimer," *Wikipedia*, http://en.wikipedia.org/wiki/Hammered_dulcimer, retrieved on April 19, 2011.

CHAPTER 5

1   Setting clocks and watches to ten past ten, or ten to two, is a frequent practice in clock circles. Originally, it was to see and access clock-face elements and wind-up key holes. It became the universal standard for displaying watches for sale, Ray Saunders recalls, when Timex adopted the practice to ensure a clear view of its brand name and logo.

CHAPTER 6

1   Charles-Edouard Guillaume, a Swiss scientist, is known for his discovery of the nickel-steel alloys he named Invar and Elinvar. Invar has a near-zero coefficient of thermal expansion, making it useful in constructing precision instruments whose dimensions need to remain constant in spite of varying temperature (like a clock pendulum). Guillaume won the 1920 Nobel Prize for physics in recognition of his metallurgical work (the only Nobel that has been granted for work related to horology).

The crucial problem in making a reliable marine chronometer was to find a resonator that remained unaffected by the changing conditions met by a ship at sea. Guillaume solved the problem with Elinvar, which has a near-zero thermal coefficient of the modulus of elasticity, making it useful in constructing instruments with springs that need to be unaffected by varying temperature, such as the marine chronometer. Elinvar is also non-magnetic, which is a secondary useful property for antimagnetic watches.

2   British mariners kept at least one chronometer on GMT (Greenwich Mean Time) in order to calculate their longitude from the Greenwich meridian, which by convention had longitude zero degrees. (This convention was internationally adopted at the International Meridian Conference of 1884.) Note that the synchronization of the chronometer on GMT did not affect shipboard time itself, which was still solar time.

3   From The Urban Dictionary, www.urbandictionary.com/define.php?term=Chronoclasm: see also http://en.wikipedia.org/wiki/Chronoclasm.

INTERESTING READING AND REFERENCES

The following list contains my suggestions for further reading on Gastown, Vancouver, clocks, and the great leveller: Time. Readers interested in my research for this book can contact me at Facebook for references, information, and conversation.

1. Bannerman, Gary, *Gastown: The 107 Years*, Vancouver: Lagoon Estates Ltd., 1974.

2. Bruton, Eric, *The History of Clocks and Watches*, New York: Crescent Books, 1989
    (first published in Great Britain in 1979 by Orbis Publishing Ltd., reprinted in 1989 by Macdonald & Co (publishers) Ltd.).

3. Davis, Chuck, ed., et al., web site for *The History of Metropolitan Vancouver*, http://www.vancouverhistory.ca.

4. Davis, Chuck, ed., *The Greater Vancouver Book: An Urban Encyclopedia*, Surrey: The Linkman Press, 1997.

5. Drew, Mary and Norman Drew, illus., *Gastown Stories*, Toronto: NC Press, 1980.

6. Falk, Dan, *In Search of Time: Journeys Along a Curious Dimension*, Toronto: McClelland & Stewart Ltd., 2008.

7. Hardwick, Walter G., *Canadian Cities Vancouver*, Collier-Macmillan Canada Ltd., 1974.

8. Klenke, Manfred, *Gastown Economic Study, 1966-1974: Commercial Rehabilitation and Revitalization of "Gastown Historic Site,"* Vancouver Department of Planning and Civic Development, 1975.

9. O'Reilly, Elizabeth, ed., *Gastown Revisited*, Community Arts Council of Vancouver, 1970.

10. A Few Good Web Sites:

    City of Vancouver Archives, http://vancouver.ca/ctyclerk/archives/
    Douglas Harper, *Online Etymology Dictionary*, http://www.etymonline.com.
    Joint Quantum Institute, http://www.jqi.umd.edu/news/
    Library & Archives Canada, http://www.collectionscanada.gc.ca/search
    National Geographic, http://ngm.nationalgeographic.com/
    National Institute of Standards and Technology (NIST), http://www.nist.gov/index.html
    Science Daily, http://www.sciencedaily.com
    Standards Council of Canada, *Consensus Magazine*, http://www.scc.ca/edocs/consensus-magazine
    Wikipedia, the free encyclopedia, http://en.wikipedia.org

PHOTO CREDITS

All photos and other graphics are used with permission of the owner or copyright holder either directly or through Wikimedia & Creative Commons Licence (http://creativecommons.org/licenses/by-sa/3.0/), GNU licence (http://commons. wikimedia.org/wiki/Commons:GNU_Free_Documentation_License_1.2), or related free licence, or because the copyright has expired, or the item is otherwise in the public domain and any use restrictions have been satisfied.

City of Vancouver Archives, Five Weeks After The Fire!: Major Matthews collection, Item Number Str P7.1, 11

Daryl R. Stennett, B.C., Canada, various Gastown Steam Clock plaques, Photos © Daryl R. Stennett, 16, 47, 72, 93, 95

Eric Miller, USA, Altoona Steam Clock, Photo © Eric Miller, Antiques Show Promotions, 108

Evan Pownall, B.C., Canada, Paralympics 2010, Photo © Evan Pownall, 121

Fred Gandolfi, Houghton Lake, MI, USA, The Market Square Steam Clock, Lake Sumter Landing, FL, Photo © 2007 by Fred Gandolfi, 108

J. Burrus/NIST, Quantum-Logic Clock, Photo Credit: J. Burrus/NIST, 118

Jayne Le Mee, Jersey Isles, G.B., The Ariadne, Photo © Jayne Le Mee, www.jaynesjersey.com, 109

Library and Archives Canada, Sir Sandford Fleming: By John Wycliffe Lowes Forster, 1892 (1850-1938), in brushpoint and red oil, Library and Archives Canada, Acc. No. 1951-566-1, 116

Lori Lanspeary, Greater Lansing Convention & Visitors Bureau, Michigan, USA, Lansing Rotary Steam Clock, Photo © Lori Lanspeary, 108

Murray from McCrae, Australia, Peter Weare's Creation, Photo © Murray from McCrae, 109

Nicole Strickland and Ken Oakes, B.C., Canada, The Connecting Piece, Article and photo © Vancouver Sun, 18

Raymond L. Saunders, B.C., Canada, Gastown and other steam clock snapshots and graphic images and other clock snapshots and graphic images. Other than cover and layout graphics by Valerie Thai, all photos and illustrations not otherwise credited on this page are the work of, or from the files of, Raymond L. Saunders, vi, 8-10, 14, 15, 17, 20-27, 29, 30, 32-48, 50, 52, 54-68, 70-73, 75, 77-80, 82-84, 86-92, 94, 95, 97-102, 104-107, 119, 120, 122

Tim Hunkin, Great Britain, Neal's Yard Steam Clock, Photo © Tim Hunkin, http://www.timhunkin.com, 107

Wikipedia/Wikimedia:
The Goseck Circle, Drawing by de:Benutzer:Rainer Zenz, 110
Goseck Palisades, WoodHenge Ringwalk, Photo by User:Wikipedia-ce, 110
Newgrange, Photo by User:Shira, 110
Avebury Circle, Photo by User:Rxfelix, 110
Stonehenge, Photo by User:nojhan for Manul Vaquero Lefanso, 111
Callanish Stones, Photo by Marta Gutowska, 111
Drombeg Stone Circle, Photo by Aaro Koskinen, 111
Towers of Chankillo, Photo by User:AgainErick, 111
Nil sine nobis, Sundial Photo by User:Daderot, 112
Sundial, Photo by User:SriMesh, 112
Su Sung's Cosmic Engine, Photo by User:PericlesofAthens (Eric Connor), 113
Clepsydra, Water clock (reconstruction), Photo by User:Marsyas, 113
Christiaan Huygens, der Astronom, auf einem Gemälde von Caspar Netscher, 1671, 114
Comput Ecclesiastique, Photo by de:Benutzer:Taxiarchos228, 114
H4 Naval Chronometer, Drawing by Fernand Bertoud, 115
The First Swiss Quartz Clock, Photo by Bajsejohannes posted by User:Rama, 117
Caesium Fountain Clock, Photo by User:METAS, 118